For Ximena

eye to eye

childhood

eye to eye
childhood

the art of growing up

in Africa, Asia, Latin America

and the Caribbean,

seen through photographs and fiction

by the region's top writers.

EYE TO EYE • CHILDREN

First published in Great Britain by
New Internationalist Publications Ltd,
55 Rectory Road, Oxford OX4 1BW, UK.

Designed by Barbara Willi-Halter for New Internationalist Publications.

BRITISH LIBRARY CATALOGUING-IN-PUBLICATION DATA
A catalogue record for this book is available from the British Library.
Hardback ISBN 1-869847-56-3

Printed by C&C Offset Printing Co. Ltd., Hong Kong.

CONTENTS

work and play

lost and found

endpiece

THE URUGUAYAN WRITER EDUARDO GALEANO dedicates his book *Football in Sun and Shadow* to 'the children who, once upon a time, years ago, crossed my path on the Calella de la Costa. They had been playing football and were singing:

> *We lost, we won,*
> *either way we had fun.'*

Children seem to know by intuition what adults can only learn to forget, that it's the fun that makes the game worth playing.

Unconfined pleasures, overwhelming passions, wild imaginings, the instinct for comedy, fairness and freedom: all these are keenly felt in childhood, essential to life, yet fade with age. Many writers say that to make their senses sharp they try not to grow up, while readers use their stories to keep alive the child in us all. This selection of fine adult writing from the South – Africa, Asia, Latin America and the Caribbean – offers a tantalizing glimpse into a world that is all around us but easily lost.

You'll find, set beside the stories, colour photographs chosen from the unique collection built up by Dexter Tiranti at New Internationalist in Oxford and Barbara Willi-Halter – the designer of this book – with the development agency Helvetas in Switzerland. Together with other European partners, they have created a series of calendars and almanacs that for more than a decade have brought life to thousands of dull walls and desks around the world. This has also encouraged people in the North to see that in the South, behind the cosmetics of tourism and the humiliation of poverty, lies another land where most of the world's people live out their daily lives with compassion and dignity in a riot of ceaseless invention.

Piecing the mass of material together has been like doing a jigsaw puzzle without the original picture. My confidence that something would emerge came largely from this book's elder sister, *eye to eye women* – edited by my colleague Vanessa Baird – which has given so much pleasure to so many readers that a sequel seemed only natural.

By reputation, photographs subvert the power of the imagination on which fiction relies. But the eye of the camera can also work with the eye of the writer and reader to produce a three-dimensional effect of great force and beauty. As you turn the pages that follow you should be able to experience this effect for yourself.

Occasionally it shows us things we might prefer not to know, or wish were not so. Other children frequently cause the worst miseries of childhood – those overwhelming, human passions can be merciless. Childhood itself is having a peculiarly bad time at the moment. In the North, far too much of it is hemmed in by the fear of predatory adult 'abuse', making this difficult territory to enter with any lightness of heart. Almost everywhere, growing up has come to mark the start of a deadly race to 'consume' at all costs. It often begins nearer to infancy than it should, and for the most part it means submitting to the dismal regulation of joyless work. Despite all this, the optimism and energy of children generally prevail, and with them our hopes for the future. Seeing childhood afresh through the eyes of the South reveals two simple, self-evident truths. The first is that life begins with equality, with identical impulses that are recognizable across all boundaries of place or culture. Children are a compelling reminder, if one were needed, of our essential humanity. The second is that, as we grow up, the mark of individuality is made by our one true possession – our imagination. With this we are amply endowed at birth. The maddening, joyful conflict in childhood between our two most precious endowments is the raw material of life, and of this book.

In a rapidly dividing world, bridges between North and South, rich and poor, young and old, work and play, are hard to find and urgently needed. Perhaps only children would dare to imagine that they might best be built with playfulness and fun.

David Ransom, Oxford, 1998

CHILDHOOD IS A MYSTERY: the soul is old, the body new, and the world complex. What a conjunction: the great unfolding in the small. This is why childhood fascinates us. It is elusive. It is elusive in us. Our childhoods have disappeared in our ageing. Memories linger; perceptions remain; but the state is gone. Gone also is its world. And childhood is a world, a separate realm. Its angles can't be relived. Its confusions are dissolved into wrong certainties. Its terrors still lurk in us, but we can't exactly locate them. We are left with observing, externally, the childhood of others. And gaze therein as into a mirror. As if childhood were generic. But childhood is specific to the child. And so when we peer into childhood's mirror we see only dim reflections; vague memories of a lost world rise in us. But we are not invited back. The borders are closed; and the country in the mirror has vanished from the world. And we are thus exiled in adulthood, either closed to, or perplexed by, mysteries.

Childhood evokes nostalgia, when it should also evoke unease. For childhood is a philosophical problem always posed to the world. The state of childhood asks questions that are seldom answered. Childhood asks us what reality really is, what the world is, where it came from, where life came from, where it goes, does the soul exist, where was the soul before birth, how many realms are there, are fairies real, do ghosts and spirits exist, why are some people lucky and others unlucky, why is there suffering, why are we here, and are there more things in the innocent-seeming spaces than we can see? Childhood is an enigma. A labyrinth. An existential question. A conundrum. A riddle more profound than the ancient riddle of the sphinx. Childhood is the home of all the great questions about life and death, reality and dream, purpose and meaning, freedom and society, the spiritual and the secular, nature and culture, education and self-discovery.

Childhood is the Nile of life; it is the Eden, the Atlantis; the living emblem of mysterious places, vanished origins, lost beginnings, all that haunts because never to be found again. It is the celebrated place of innocence, of the first evils, of the first falls, of the first sufferings, of the first floods, and of the first civilisations within each human spirit.

It is the Nile whose source leads to the perplexing, the illimitable. Out of childhood rises the sphinx that is the adult, who cannot now pose its own riddle, much less answer it. And yet, from this Nile, from childhood, what personality is already present! Where did that distinct self come from; in what place intangible had it been gestating; in what universities of the invisible had its mind been preparing? Its angles on the world surprise; its observations ought to have a place in the academies of the world. It is not just the innocence of childhood that should command our attention. It is also its unseeing, or rather its pure seeing, uncontaminated by structures of thought. That way childhood sometimes has of perceiving events asequentially, tangentially, as though through the corridors of their minds clear winds of intuition blow, hinting at the essential unreality of time and space. How like a great unlearning childhood is; small wonder all the sages through time use the state of childhood to speak of the highest things, the highest peaks of cultural and spiritual attainment.

2

Childhood ought to terrify us with gentle wonder, ought to make us feel curiously humble. Childhood gazed at is akin to genius: there is simply no accounting for its everlasting appeal, its charm, its unfathomability. I am not being sentimental. I am speaking here of an aspect of childhood that lingers in the depths of the mind, like an imperishable melody. I am not speaking here of the other aspects of spoilt or conditioned or wretched childhoods that can be seen in nasty little boys or horrid little girls. I speak of the childhood seen out of the corner of the eyes. I speak of the conjunction of its unco-ordination and its magic; its serenity and its confusions. Its multiple perspective. Its freedom. Its lack of freedom.

That is why childhood also has something tragic about it. For childhood is the place, the country, the only country in the world, where tyranny rules absolutely. And of necessity. The child is moulded: that is the beginning of its fall. The sinking of its Atlantis. The loss of its Eden. To the child the world is named. Explained. Mis-explained. Seamed with errors. Made smaller. Made plainer. Made too complicated. Narrowed. Filled with suspicion, dogma, envy. Wonder is driven out. Mystery is hounded away from the fabric of reality. The tendency to question is turned into a tendency to be closed; the inclination to trust is warped into an inclination to fear; flexibility is mis-represented as weakness; sensitivity is distorted into timidity. The child is shaped – or dare one say mis-shaped: its open form is closed off; its river canalised; its mind, trapped; its spirit, caged; its playfulness, forced; its joys, made suspect; its laughter, imprisoned.

The child could be shaped open, could be taught to value all peoples, to respect all races and creeds; but the child is taught to be suspicious of difference, different peoples, different religions, different ways. A flower is thus changed into a thorn. A river into a brook. A garden into a wasteland. The child is enveloped into the forms of a particular culture, when it could also be opened out to be at home in the world, with all its diversity. For when the child was born, it was born into the world, the open world. The stage of the world. Not the ghetto. Or the corner. Or the palace. Or the villa. But the world of men and women, of history and dreams, of the limited and the limitless, the village and the ocean, the backyard and the sky. And all books, and all thoughts, and all music and art and temples and concrete dreams that have been created by the perpetual pilgrimage of humanity through the dusty roads of time.

But adults then close the open world off, with veils, words, signs, mind-sets, and terror. But the child is more open than that: reared by a wolf in legend, the child becomes wolf-like. Reared by others, the child has others within it.

Childhood is a mixture of the tragic and the magical because it is the only time that the mind has no boundaries. Fairies were as real as fires. Fables were true. The world was a dream. And reality was a perpetual invention. And then the snake creeps in; and slowly corruption creeps in too; and the dream dies. Hemingway writes somewhere of rich men and women in their yachts who weep at night because they can't sleep as purely as they did when they were children. More controversially Blake writes somewhere that education is a sin. 'Improvement makes strait roads; but the crooked roads without improvement are roads of genius.' Some people loathe their childhood because they were betrayed by it. I know of childhoods so severe, so brutalised, so poverty-stricken, so crushed with oppression and violence that it's a wonder the children didn't become mass-murderers. They turned out relatively sane. This continues to puzzle me. Even in the hardest of people there lurks something of childhood's elusive twilight; it may be distorted, but it's there. And

it comes out in what they love, what they are sentimental about, or what they hate.

3

Childhood: being under the care of those who are generally ill-qualified to be parents. People ought to learn to be parents before they become parents. It should be more than just a biological inevitability.

Childhood: focus of love – real love – confused love –

Childhood: the meeting place of an endless chain of failures and fears, disorders and disasters, marvels and joys, the hidden narrative of ancestors. Inheritors of concentrated fictions invisible. Every child is an entire literature. All tragedies, comedies and epics are already resident in its birth.

Childhood: a state that we project onto, notions of innocence, wisdom, purity...

Childhood: a lottery, Chardin's game of cards, a gamble, the luck of the draw, the obscure mathematics of destiny, or karma; an unspecified punishment or an unnamed blessing – for deserving the parents you have, the family you're stuck with, or the life you were born into.

Childhood: a time also of cruelties, tearing off the wings of butterflies, cutting up worms, ganging up on the weakest, ganging up against the newcomer, the strange one, the one of a different hue or colour; the peculiar intolerance of childhood; the unqualified ego of the state; the games, the toy guns, the locking up of the smallest in a shed and then forgetting...

Childhood: the place of all society's experiments, its disastrous ideas of consciousness engineering.

Childhood: the place where so many seeds and notions are planted in us, and watered with the loving hands of our parents, and become full-grown trees of appalling prejudices, deeply-held secret resentments, fiercely guarded dragons of suspicions, hydra-headed monsters of superstitions about others, all of these lovingly or bitterly planted in us and absorbed by us with all the full reverence and unquestioning acceptance we accorded our parents when our minds were young, and theirs. It is a difficult thing indeed to free our minds of the errors of our parents; for it amounts to re-writing our childhood, tearing down its mysterious palaces, stripping our parents of their mythical place in us, of their wisdom, conceding them a certain amount of ordinariness, like any other parent of one's age group that one might think of as a bit of a fool and yet to their child is a god... who can disarrange the fragile garden of childhood, and not make themselves the drier for it...

Childhood: In literature childhood is an invention, a creation, a state constructed. The literature of childhood properly is either historical fiction, or an aspect of imaginative reconstruction. Childhood itself is a fairytale taking place in a chaos. Childhood is not aware of itself as childhood.

Childhood: Notice how late the literature of childhood appeared in the ancient world. The literature of childhood seems to suggest that society has passed its phase of childhood, its phase of unconscious consciousness, its period of myths and legends, its time of living fables, of heroic deeds, of difficulties, of beginnings. This literature suggests a new phase of nostalgia, of loss. The literature of childhood signifies that in a nation or a people its golden age is over. They look back who have crossed the hill. When a society has lost its way, it looks back thus – to childhood, to origins, to arcadias. This signifies chaos. A longing for simplicity, away from confusion.

A literature of childhood is an implicit condemnation of the present. It can often be a quiet – or an explosive – political act. A scream woven into a melody. A beautiful song thrown into the face of tyranny. A transfigured form of guerilla warfare against the psyche of repression. A howl from the heart of wounded innocence. Exile from the intolerable present.

Childhood: Nations are best when you can still see something of the openness of the child in the grown-ups: a wisdom that arcs towards mature simplicity, like ancient temples.

4

Our childhoods pass obscure judgements on us. Who, looking at a picture of themselves as a child, does not hear a faint whisper say: this is what you were, and look at what you have become? We always let down the majestic promise inherent in our childhood. But we are not entirely sure in what way; the failure eludes us somehow. Childhood seems to promise so much, much that is unspecified. An eternal twinge of failure awaits the man or woman who can meet the child that they were: for childhood seems to say that anything is

possible, and the golden ages can be made in our time, within those lustrous eyes. And then the child becomes the person you are, here, now. Whoever you may be.

How fallen are the promises, how lowly are the glories! Childhood is the enchanted judgement of the world, of society, and what we have let it become.

5

Childhood is the father and mother of humanity: in its mysterious estate lie our greatest secrets; our cures; our hopes; our redemptions. In its mortal coil lie our flaws, our weaknesses, the earliest programming of our complex natures.

Childhood is humanity's secret. If you want to understand a nation study the way it treats its children, the way it educates them, the way it moulds them. Study the children themselves. Are the children suspicious of the other, of different peoples, those of different colours? Then their parents are. Then society is. Are the children open to other, to differences? Then so, largely, are their parents. Their society. Children are the true thoughts of their nation, their people, their class – the true thoughts, untrammelled by diplomacy, politeness, politics, and social manners. Children betray nations. Children betray families. Or they redeem them. They reveal them. They show what is good, what is true, what is pure, what is striven for, and what is natural in nations, and in families.

6

Childhood is also the future of all, not its past. All great things incline us towards a higher childhood. Atlantis lives on in our imagination, and much can be learned from it. Eden has been transmuted into a future destination, made by our collective will and goodness, shaped by our hearts that yearn for a world where the unsuspected genius within us can live and unfold. Childhood is the great puzzle, the marvellous symbol, the emblem of the quintessence, the magic mirror, the silent Grail, the missing key to our futures. This is why the literature of childhood is so important. It reveals to us our true hidden forgotten selves. It tells us who we are, and why. It lights the way to the future. It dispels the shadows of the past. It shines a light on society. It brings back into our increasingly arid and closed minds the magic that dreams sometimes have. It makes some forgotten joy tremble in us. It re-awakens the heart. It makes us want to dream again, be free again, to reach for childhood's elusive promise of a better self. It makes us want to transform the world, and to be happy.

And with the best writing about childhood something else happens. The world is made new. Fables become real. Time and space are revealed as illusions. A vaster mysterious power flows through the mind. One can fly. For a long moment, all things are possible – why not? The mind conceiving them makes them real. Schopenhauer saw childhood as more concerned with discovery. We discover the world again. We discover ourselves – at least we are tempted to begin the journey. And then the closed circle becomes open again...

7

Novalis puts it beautifully. 'Where children are, there is a golden age.' Childhood is the golden age of humanity. We invent it in retrospect, with wonder woven in.

Through the artist flows the childhood of the world, the golden ages. In their best works we catch glimpses of the kingdom that childhood hints at. And we know that what we have glimpsed is not magic, or art, or enchantment. We know, in some obscure way, that the kingdom is real. This is what haunts us forever.

O childhood, O initiation and birthplace of the world; the acorn, the seed, the ocean, the crossroad of past and future, the meeting place of lives; where what was is forgotten progressively, and where what will be is learned intermittently.

Ben Okri, London, 1998

fun and fear

HAVE IT, MAKE IT OR POKE IT AT SOMEONE. You can do all sorts of things with fun if you know how, and children soon get the knack. But fear is never far away — fear of the unknown or of unpredictable grown-ups. That can be part of the fun. Eduardo Galeano joins the world of make-believe with the children of Ollantaytambo, Peru — while on the streets of Bahia, Brazil, Jorge Amado's stately female figures of fun run a gauntlet of impish catcalls. But beware! Fascinating snakes lurk in the grass around Camara Laye's family home in Guinea. Fearful of drought, Bessie Head lies in wait for the rains in Botswana. Jung Chang finds out for herself what really happens, despite all the warnings, if you swallow an orange pip, while a ladder would have spared Zaynab Alkali a painful confession after a night out in Nigeria.

IT HAPPENED AT THE ENTRANCE to the town of Ollantaytambo, near Cuzco. I had detached myself from a group of tourists and was standing alone looking at the stone ruins in the distance when a small boy from the neighbourhood, skinny and ragged, came over to ask if I would give him a pen. I couldn't give him my pen because I was using it to write down all sorts of boring notes, but I offered to draw a little pig for him on his hand.

Suddenly the word got around. I was surrounded by a throng of little boys demanding at the top of their lungs that I draw animals on their little hands cracked by the dirt and cold, their skin of burnt leather: one wanted a condor and one a snake, others preferred little parrots and owls, and some asked for a ghost or a dragon.

Then, in the middle of this racket, a little waif who barely cleared a yard off the ground showed me a watch drawn in black ink on his wrist.

'An uncle of mine who lives in Lima sent it to me,' he said.

'And does it keep good time?' I asked him.

'It's a bit slow,' he admitted.

from **THE BOOK OF EMBRACES** by Eduardo Galeano, Uruguay

These children in
Ollantaytambo, Peru,
are watchful onlookers
at celebrations for the
foundation of their
school.

Photo: Mary Jelliffe

WHEN THE TWO WOMEN came out of the fashionable eleven o'clock Mass at the Church of St Francis one clear Sunday morning in June, luminous and cool, and with resolute steps crossed the Terreiro de Jesus, making for the narrow old streets of Pelourinho, street urchins began dancing the samba in a circle, beating out the syncopated rhythm on empty guava paste tins:

Hey, lady
With the big bum!
Hey, the big bum!
The fine bum!

Dona Norma turned to her companion, grumbling: 'Those brats – why don't they go and fool around with their mothers' bums?'
Perhaps it was a mere coincidence, and the kids had not been referring to their callipygous exuberance; but be that as it may, Dona Norma glared in terrifying fashion at the impudent mockers. A glare which instantly turned tender as she discovered in the circle a little boy of about three, ragged, bleary-eyed, and runny-nosed: 'Look how cute, Flor, how pretty that little rascal dancing there is...'
Dona Flor looked at the gang of ragged children. Many others were scattered about the overflowing square, running between the legs of itinerant photographers, trying to swipe an orange, a lime, a tangerine, a hog plum, a *sapote* from the vendors' baskets. They were applauding a barker selling miracle-working pharmaceutical products, with a snake coiled around his neck, a repulsive necktie. They were begging alms at the doors of the five churches on the square, practically assaulting the well-to-do parishioners. They were exchanging wisecracks with sleepy whores, young for the most part, patrolling the park in the hope of a hasty morning client. A swarm of ragged, bold children, the offspring of the women of the district, without father or home. They lived in a state of abandonment; they would soon be delinquents, for whom the police stations would hold no secrets.
Dona Flor shivered. She had come to carry away one of those children, newly born, and in that way protect it from itself and its mother. But on seeing the children running loose around Terreiro Square, her heart was filled with pity, with a pure and noble emotion; at that moment, if it had been in her power, she would have adopted them all.

from **DONA FLOR AND HER TWO SISTERS** by Jorge Amado, translated by Harriet de Onís, Brazil

'Sugar-cane brew crushed while you wait' is the gist of the writing on the wall in this run-down area of Bahia, north-east Brazil. A premature career as entrepreneurs has to replace education for many children, as schools are scarce.

Photo: Herman Bertiau

I WAS A LITTLE BOY playing round my father's hut. How old would I have been at that time? I cannot remember exactly. I still must have been very young: five, maybe six years old. My mother was in the workshop with my father, and I could just hear their familiar voices above the noise of the anvil and the conversation of the customers.

Suddenly I stopped playing, my whole attention fixed on a snake that was creeping round the hut. He really seemed to be 'taking a turn' round the hut. After a moment I went over to him. I had taken in my hand a reed that was lying in the yard – there were always some lying around; they used to get broken off the fence of plaited reeds that marked the boundary of our compound – and I thrust this reed into the reptile's mouth. The snake did not try to get away: he was beginning to enjoy our little game; he was slowly swallowing the reed; he was devouring it, I thought, as if it were some delicious prey, his eyes glittering with voluptuous bliss; and inch by inch his head was drawing nearer to my hand. At last the reed was almost entirely swallowed up, and the snake's jaws were terribly close to my fingers.

I was laughing, I had not the slightest fear, and now I know that the snake would not have hesitated much longer before burying his fangs in my fingers if, at that moment, Damany, one of the apprentices, had not come out of the workshop. The apprentice shouted to my father, and almost at once I felt myself lifted off my feet: I was safe in the arms of one of my father's friends!

There was a terrible commotion going on all round me; my mother was shouting harder than anyone; and she gave me a few sharp slaps. I began to weep, more upset by the sudden uproar than by the blows I had received. A little later, when I had calmed down a little and the shouting had died down around me, my mother solemnly warned me never to play such a game again; and I promised, although I could not really see where the danger in it lay.

My father's hut was near the workshop, and I would often play there beneath the veranda that ran round the outside. It was my father's private hut. It was built like all our huts, of mud that had been pounded and moulded into bricks with water; it was round, and proudly helmeted with thatch. It was entered by a rectangular doorway. Inside, a tiny window let in a thin shaft of daylight. On the right there was the bed, made of beaten earth like the bricks, spread with a simple wicker-work mat on which was a pillow stuffed with kapok. At the rear of the hut, right under the window where the light was strongest, were the tool-boxes. On the left were the *boubous* and the prayer-rugs. Finally, at the head of the bed, hanging over the pillow and watching over my father's slumber, there was a series of pots that contained extracts from plants and the bark of trees. These pots all had metal lids and they were profusely and curiously garlanded with chaplets of cowrie shells; it did not take me long to discover that they were the most important things in the hut: they contained the magic charms, those mysterious liquids that keep evil spirits at bay, and, smeared on the body, make it invulnerable to black magic, to all kinds of black magic. My father, before he went to bed, never failed to smear his body with a little of each liquid, first one, then another, for each charm had its own particular property: but exactly *what* property I do not know: I left my father's house too soon.

From the veranda under which I played I could keep an eye on the workshop opposite, and they for their part could keep an eye on me. This workshop was the main building in our compound. That is where my father was generally to be found, supervising the work, forging the most important items himself, or repairing delicate mechanisms; here it was that he received his friends and his customers, so that the place resounded with noise from morning to night. Moreover, everyone entering or leaving our compound had to pass through the workshop, so that there was a perpetual coming and going, though no one ever seemed to be in a hurry: each one would pause to have a word with my father and spend a few moments watching the work in hand. Sometimes I would draw near the door, but I rarely went in, for everyone used to frighten me there, and I would run away as soon as anyone tried to lay hands on me. It was not until very much later that I got into the habit of crouching in a corner of the workshop and watching the fire blazing in the forge.

My private domain at that time consisted of the veranda that ran round the outside of my father's hut; and the orange tree that grew in the middle of the compound.

As soon as you had crossed the workshop and gone through the door at the back, you could see the orange tree. If I compare it with the giants of our native forests, the tree was not very big, but its mass of glossy leaves used to cast a dense shadow that was a cool refuge from the blazing sun. When it was in flower, a heady perfume was wafted over the entire compound. When the fruit appeared, we were allowed only to look: we had to possess our souls in patience until they were →

Adodou Ouedraogo poses with his family, in the village of Silmiougou, Burkina Faso, West Africa. His parents are proud of him — he's the first in the village to go on to higher education.

Photo: James Nelson

ripe. Then my father, who, as the head of the family – a family of innumerable members – governed the compound, would give orders to pick them. The men who did the picking brought their baskets one by one to my father, who shared them out among the inhabitants of the compound, his neighbours and his customers; after that we were permitted to help ourselves from the baskets, as much as we liked! My father was an open-handed and, in fact, a lavish giver; no matter who turned up, he would share our meals; and as I could never keep up with the speed at which such guests used to eat, I might have remained everlastingly hungry if my mother had not taken the precaution of putting my share on one side.

'Sit here,' she would say, 'and eat, for your father's crazy.'

Still she did not look upon such guests with too kindly an eye; there were too many of them for her liking, all bent on filling their bellies at her expense. My father, for his part, ate very sparingly; he was a very abstemious man.

We lived near the railway track. The trains travelled along outside the fence of plaited reeds which marked the confines of our compound; in fact they ran so close to it that sparks from the engines would sometimes set fire to the palisade, and we all would have to rush to put it out at once, if we did not want to see the whole thing go up in flames. These alarms, rather frightening, but rather exciting too, made me watch every train that went by; and even when there was not a train in sight – for at the time the traffic on the railroad depended entirely on the river traffic, which was very irregular – I would go and spend long periods just looking at the gleaming metal rails. They always glittered cruelly under the fierce sun, for at this point there was no foliage to diminish its intensity. Baked by the sun from early morning, the ballast of red stone was burningly hot: so hot in fact that the oil which fell from the engines was immediately evaporated, leaving not the slightest trace. Was it this oven-like warmth or the oil, the inescapable smell of the oil, which attracted the snakes? I do not know. The fact is that I often came across snakes crawling over the sun-baked ballast; and inevitably the snakes used to creep into the compound.

Ever since the day I had been forbidden to play with snakes, I would run to my mother as soon as I saw one.

'There's a snake!' I would cry.

'What, another?' my mother would shout.

And she would come running out to see what sort of a snake it was. If it was just a snake like any other snake – actually, they were all quite different! – she would beat it to death at once; and, like all the women of our country, she would work herself up into a frenzy, beating the snake to pulp, whereas the men would content themselves with a single hard blow, neatly struck.

One day, however, I noticed a little black snake with a strikingly marked body that was proceeding leisurely in the direction of the workshop. I ran to warn my mother, as usual. But as soon as my mother saw the black snake she said to me gravely:

'My son, this one must not be killed: he is not as other snakes, and will not harm you; you must never interfere with him.'

Everyone in our compound knew that this snake must not be killed; excepting myself, and, I suppose, my little playmates, who were still just ignorant children.

'This snake,' my mother added, 'is your father's guiding spirit.'

I gazed dumbfounded at the little snake. He was proceeding calmly towards the workshop; he was moving gracefully, very sure of himself, and almost as if conscious of his immunity; his body, black and brilliant, glittered in the harsh light of the sun. When he reached the workshop, I noticed for the first time, cut out level with the ground, a small hole in the wall. The snake disappeared through this hole.

'Look,' said my mother, 'the serpent is going to pay your father a visit.'

from **THE AFRICAN CHILD** by Camara Laye, Guinea

Half-sisters Até and Ablai (carrying her baby sister Khady) play with porridge. They belong to an extended family with 13 children in the village of Daybassar, Senegal.

Photo: Michel Szulc-Krzyzanowski

LOVING AND LOVABLE
trying / temperamental
irrepressible / irascible
but always adorable.....

who are these monsters
who often drive us
to the gates of asylums
with their tantrums?

who turn our bedrooms
into battlefields strewn
with blankets & toys
but who also transmute
the dross of afternoons
into Le Carre thrillers
with stratagems & ploys.

Who can resurrect jaded eyes
to the wonders of a sunflower;
take us on a trip
to the stars with their
bubbly tales and laughter
then plummet us into a pit
of anxiety with a rising fever.

Loving and lovable
trying / temperamental
irrepressible / irascible
but always adorable
these space invaders
we call – CHILDREN !

from **BROKEN BUDS** by Cecil Rajendra, Malaysia

Testing out the
merchandise for their
parents, who own this
shop selling household
provisions in Loei,
Thailand.

Photo:
Janet Wishnetsky

ALL DAY LONG I lie asleep under the thorn tree, and the desert is on this side of me and on that side of me. I have no work to do. We are all waiting for the rain, as we cannot plough without rain. I think the rain has gone away again, like last year. We had a little rain in November, but December has gone, and now it is January; and each day we have been sitting here, waiting for rain: my mother, my grandmother, my grandfather, my cousin Lebenah, and my sister and her little baby. If it were to rain my grandfather would push the plough and my cousin Lebenah would pull the oxen across the great miles of our land. We women would follow behind, sowing maize, millet, pumpkin and watermelon seed. I feel great pity for my family, and other families. I wonder why we sit here like this. Each day the sun is hot, hot in the blue sky. Each day the water pool of November rain gets smaller. Soon we will have to leave the land and return to the village.

In the village we have a politician who takes the people up on the hill to pray for rain. He wears a smart suit and has a big black car and a beautiful deep African voice. His mind is quick and moves from one thing to another. He can pray, and cry, and speak politics all at once. People always expect the rain to fall the minute after he has stopped praying and crying. They call him the one who has shaken God loose. Actually, I have not been sleeping the whole day. I am trying to learn English. My cousin Lebenah tells me that things are changing in Africa, and that it is necessary for women to improve themselves. I love my cousin Lebenah so much that I do anything he tells me to do. He tells me that English is the best language to learn, as many books have been written in English, and that there is no end to the knowledge that can be gained from them. He gave me a geography book and I have read it over and over. I am puzzled and afraid. Each year the sun is more cruel. Each year the rain becomes less and less. Each year more and more of our cattle die. The only animal that survives is the goat. It can eat anything and we eat the goat. Without the goat, I do not know what we would do. It is all about us, like the family. It has the strangest eyes. They are big and yellow, and the pupil is a black streak right across the yellow ball of the eye.

I am trying to improve myself too, as I am very afraid that I may have an illegitimate baby like my elder sister. My family will suffer much. And the child too. It may die. There is never enough food and we are always hungry. It is not so easy for a woman to have too many babies when she has improved her mind. She has to think about how she will feed the baby, clothe it, and wash it. My sister's baby is lovely, though. He laughs a lot for no reason.

My geography book makes me wonder and wonder. It tells me that water is formed by hydrogen and oxygen. I wonder so much about that. If we had green things everywhere, they might help make the oxygen to make the rain. The soil is very fertile. If there is only a little rain, green things come out everywhere, and many strange flowers. How can we live like this? Here are our bags with the seeds of maize, and millet, and the land is as hard as stone.

Tomorrow the sun will rise, quietly. The many birds in the bush will welcome it. I will not. Alone, without the help of rain, it is cruel, killing and killing. All day we look on it, like on death. Then, at evening, all is as gentle as we are. Mother roasts goat meat over the coals of the wood fire. Sister feeds her baby. Grandfather and cousin Lebenah talk quietly to each other about little things. The stars spread across the sky and bend down at the horizon. The quiet talk of grandfather and cousin Lebenah seem to make earth and heaven come together. I do not know what we would do if we all did not love one another, because tomorrow the sun will rise again.

from **TALES OF TENDERNESS AND POWER** by Bessie Head, Botswana

Goats are the lifeblood of the San people of the Kalahari Desert in Botswana

Photo: Angela Fisher/ Robert Estall Picture Library

IN THE SUMMER OF 1956 my grandmother returned to Chengdu. The first thing she did was to rush to the nurseries and take us back to my mother's place. My grandmother had a fundamental dislike of nurseries. She said children could not be properly looked after in a group. My sister and I looked all right, but as soon as we spotted her, we screamed and demanded to go home. The two boys were another matter: Jin-ming's teacher complained that he was terribly withdrawn, and would not let any adult touch him. He only asked, quietly but obstinately, for his old nurse. My grandmother burst into tears when she saw Xiao-hei. He looked like a wooden puppet, with a meaningless grin on his face. Wherever he was put, whether sitting or standing, he would just remain there, motionless. He did not know how to ask to go to the lavatory, and did not even seem to be able to cry. My grandmother swept him up into her arms and he instantly became her favourite.

Back at my mother's apartment, my grandmother gave vent to her anger and incomprehension. In between her tears she called my father and my mother 'heartless parents'. She did not know that my mother had no choice.

Because my grandmother could not look after all four of us, the two older ones, my sister and I, had to go to a nursery during the week. Every Monday morning, my father and his bodyguard would lift us onto their shoulders and carry us off howling, kicking, and tearing their hair.

This went on for some time. Then, subconsciously, I developed a way of protesting. I began to fall ill at the nursery, with high fevers which alarmed the doctors. As soon as I was back home, my illness miraculously evaporated. Eventually, my sister and I were allowed to stay at home.

For my grandmother, all flowers and trees, the clouds and the rain were living beings with a heart and tears and a moral sense. We would be safe if we followed the old Chinese rule for children, *ting-hua* ('heeding the words', being obedient). Otherwise all sorts of things would happen to us. When we ate oranges my grandmother would warn us against swallowing the seeds. 'If you don't listen to me, one day you won't be able to get into the house. Every little seed is a baby orange tree, and he wants to grow up just like you. He'll grow quietly inside your tummy, up and up, then one day, *Ai-ya!* There he is, out from the top of your head! He'll grow leaves, and bear more oranges, and he'll become taller than our door...'

The thought of carrying an orange tree on my head fascinated me so much that one day I deliberately swallowed a seed - one, no more. I did not want an orchard on my head: that would be too heavy. For the whole day, I anxiously felt my skull every other minute to see whether it was still in one piece. Several times I almost asked my grandmother whether I would be allowed to eat the oranges on my head, but I checked myself so that she would not know I had been disobedient. I decided to pretend it was an accident when she saw the tree. I slept very badly that night. I felt something was pushing up against my skull.

*from **WILD SWANS** by Jung Chang, China*

Life for the Toktobik family in China's Kazakh Autonomous State has not changed much since the days of Tamburlaine and Ghengis Khan. The people still travel between the Gobi Desert and their mountain pastures and live in a *kigizuy* – a felt tent furnished with carpets and cushions. A good place for telling tall stories, too.

Photo:
Sarah Errington/
The Hutchison Library

BEYOND THE BELT OF THE HORIZON
our wrists are squeezed
and without a word the clouds disperse
further and further
squeezing our wrists.

our heads emptied
into the generation we brought into the world,
all anointed with prison lime.
our fruits grow without flavour or smell
and we accuse them of betraying the seed
but they, innocent, know nothing of betrayal.

they are children of the generation of fear
and from the moment they saw the sun,
it was already dark during the daytime.
but from some order they got the courage
to walk in the streets with empty hands.

our children are fruits that do not reflect
beyond the table where dinner happens
when they're not just the looks of a frightened lizard
hearing footsteps and hiding in the bushes on the look-out
for their share of rubbish.

They are children of the generation of fear
whose smothered scream blocked the artery,
and pressure was brought down
through the emptying out of thought.
they want flowers and hymns in my blood
but in my blood there is only blood
and fear of speaking out and fear of remaining silent

because our children

are our children
and we need them to be the children of their times
these times we have built
with silence and death.

without horizons, this time is cold
without horizons, this time is ugly
for our children.

It's necessary to plant and plough the land now
when all has been forgotten so it can last.
like the ancient oaks
just providing shadow.

the generation of fear files past and wants to think
wants to say, tell, recall.
only history plants consciousness
in the opaque moment.
desperate embroiderer, the generation of fear
hunts for scraps, dyes bits and pieces
and tries to build,
shows its face and hands out the old outburst.

how difficult it's become to be
but it was always difficult to be in vain.

from **THE GENERATION OF FEAR** by Lourdes Teodoro, Brazil

Forced from the land, a floating household lies grounded on mud in the estuary of the River Amazon, Brazil, and is in constant danger of being swept away. Drinking water has to be fetched by children from great distances because the water of the river carries many agents of human disease.

Photo: Julio Etchart

THE NEXT MORNING Baba called all the children, except the small ones. He stood, feet apart and arms akimbo, scowling at a large opening in the fence behind Mama's hut. When he saw that they had all assembled, he turned to face them.

'Who went out last night?' he asked, looking at them one by one in his usual direct way. Nobody answered him and he repeated the question twice, his face darkening with anger. Awa gave Li a warning glance.

'I am talking to all of you. Have you lost your tongues?'

Still no one said anything. They looked at each other furtively. Above their heads a long oiled whip hung loosely from the end of a bamboo pole. The silence was becoming intolerable. Suddenly, Li opened her mouth but was forestalled by Awa.

'Nobody went out as far as I know,' she said uncertainly.

'Then can you explain the gaping hole, Awa?'

'No, Father.'

'A dog could have done that,' Li blundered and regretted it immediately. Her father might be a short-sighted bigot, but he was no fool.

'Uhmm, a dog. You really want me to believe a dog made this neat opening, do you?' he reached for the oiled whip as he spoke. Sule gave Li a look that seemed to say, 'Keep quiet, let me handle this'.

Sule had known Li went out the previous night. Frustrated at the thought that all his friends were at the dance, he himself had been unable to sleep. He had tossed on his bed for hours, his heart throbbing in rhythm to the drumbeat. He knew the dance steps and ached to try them in the dancing arena. He had thought of stealing out over the fence, but dispelled such thoughts immediately. The dance wasn't worth the disgrace.

At midnight he had gone behind his mother's hut to smoke a little to ease the tension. He could not smoke inside his hut because Baba had a disturbing habit of barging in on him – a sort of check on his daily habits. He had thought of school and wished the holidays were over. School was much better. He lit a cigarette and immediately nipped at it, burning his finger in the process. A sudden rustling sound had scared him. He quickly dropped the cigarette and stepped on it. He braced himself for a confrontation with his father, but instead came face to face with Li.

'God in heaven, small one, you scared my insides,' he exclaimed, bending low and searching for the cigarette in the clear moonlight.

'See what you have cost me,' he raised his hand to her nose. 'A costly stick and a burnt finger.'

'Ssh, son-of-my-mother, Father might hear us,' Li whispered, coming closer to him. 'I've been to the dance,' she said excitedly. 'I will tell you all about it in the morning.'

'Uhmm,' Sule grunted. 'To the dance, Li?'

'Say nothing to anybody or...' she paused for a while, 'I might just be tempted to mention this.' She touched the cigarette.

'You know I won't,' Sule said soberly, 'but I am afraid for you though. You shouldn't have broken the fence.' He moved closer and examined the fence. 'You are really empty-headed. You should have climbed over the fence.'

'Allah! That's an idea,' she exclaimed, 'I'll remember that another time.'

'If you survive this time,' Sule said. 'Now wait,' he took hold of her arm as she made to leave. 'What are you going to do about the fence?'

'Mend it, of course,' she said easily.

'Before morning?'

She thought for a minute and said, 'I don't know. I guess it'll have to wait until morning.'

'Until he sees you, you mean?'

'I will have to get up at cockcrow'

'Wake me up and I will help you.'

'Thank you, son-of-my-mother.'

'Don't worry, little sister. Aren't we friends?'

'Plotters,' Li said and they laughed quietly. They both heard a slight cough from the direction of Baba's room and stole away quietly. In the morning Baba had forestalled them, much to their horror. They had overslept.

Awa looked at the oiled whip and shot a glance at Li. She too knew who had gone out last night, although she hadn't known how until now. At midnight, she had got up to look for her blanket and had found Li's bed empty. 'Useless child,' Awa had thought. 'She must have gone after that worthless beggar.'

Now, standing in front of Baba who was angry beyond description, Awa wondered what Li saw in that stranger to risk their father's anger. Good-looking, yes, but what woman needed a man for his face? For that was all he had, a face. In those clothes he looked like a market beggar. Why, the shorts hardly covered his buttocks. And he called himself 'the son-of-the-chief'. Awa stifled a giggle at the train of →

The Kuasi peoples of north-east Ghana are very conscious of traditional values. The cornerstone of Kuasi society is the family compound, built in a circle amidst the millet fields.

Photo: Ulrich Schweizer

her thoughts. 'No,' she said to herself. 'The man isn't worth the trouble, Li would be in serious trouble if Baba found out. God knows, the girl has the brain of a chicken. She could have climbed over the fence.' For some strange reason she was glad this had happened. If Li was punished, she thought, she might forget about the stranger. But why did she dislike Habu so much? She tried asking herself that question. Surely it wasn't because he looked poor? What had poverty to do with it? After all, no one in her family could present a better picture.

'Awa,' Baba cut into her thoughts.

'Yes, Father.'

'Are you sure you know nothing about the hole?'

'No, Father.' She was glad he hadn't asked if she had gone to the dance. She wouldn't have known how to answer that.

'I know Sani slept in his mother's hut, because he was ill,' he began. 'Mari is only six and afraid of the dark. The twins are only four years old, not to talk of Bata who is still a baby,' he pushed on, looking at them one by one. His eyes landed momentarily on Sani's immediate senior. 'Where were you last night, Becki Hirwa?'

'I was in bed, Baba. You can ask Mama,' she said and their father nodded, convinced. Li knew what was coming. Baba wasn't getting any answers, so he had started a calculated process of elimination, bent on finding the truant. Well, she would have to own up, she thought. It was the price she had to pay for the clandestine meeting. She braced herself for the ordeal by taking a deep breath. Her eyes dilated – half with fear, half with expectation – as Baba's eyes settled on her finally.

'What about you, Li? Were you at the dance?'

'I was, Father.' Again, Li was forestalled – this time by Sule's deep voice which jolted everybody. Li looked up in surprise. Sule was shielding her. Awa looked from Li to Sule and back, obviously confused.

'I had to go,' Sule was speaking. 'All my friends were there. I could not sleep.'

There was a charged silence. No one moved or spoke. Finally Baba moved in Sule's direction. He stood and faced his son and they stared at each other. Baba had been taken unawares. He knew that Sule was capable of this sort of thing but, somehow, he had suspected Li this time. He could not say exactly why. Was it the mad glint in her eyes when she had said it could be a dog, or was it the furtive glances? May be she was trying to protect Sule, or was it the other way round? Whichever way it was, Baba knew someone was lying somewhere along the line. What worried him now was, what was he to do with this man-child? He was a man now and it wasn't just his age, but what he stood for. He could beat Awa easily if she erred, now matter how old she was, but not Sule, his firstborn malechild. And to beat a man for going out to dance at night was outrageous. He decided to give him a chance to apologise. That way both could salvage their pride.

'I am ashamed of you breaking a fence like that,' he said and waited. Silence. He fixed Sule with a hard stare and with his eyes begged him to apologise, but Sule stared back, a new kind of look creeping into his eyes. It was a defiant look as if he was challenging his father to a duel. Baba was suddenly infuriated and said to himself, 'What has come over the children of today? They are not only rebellious but completely immodest. Now what am I to do with Sule?' The others sensed Baba's dilemma and moved closer.

Li no longer looked fidgety. Her eyes grew bold. She was beginning to enjoy the drama. Sule had covered up for her, but Li knew very well that Sule's heroism was on his own account. There was no way he could have escaped their father's wrath this day, because Li wasn't one to take any beating alone and Sule was well aware of that.

'I went out and so did big sister Awa,' she would have blurted out. 'As for big brother Sule, he smoked something awful.'

Nevertheless, Li had her good points. Now that Sule had covered for her first, she was going to do the same. If Baba insisted on beating Sule, she was going to confuse the whole issue by confessing. That way, Baba would never know who actually went out, and he wasn't one to punish anyone if in doubt. Li smiled wickedly. It seemed to her that was one of Baba's few virtues.

from **THE STILLBORN** by Zaynab Alkali, Nigeria

joy and sorrow

THE PLEASURES OF CHILDHOOD are sharpened by the pain of growing up. Carlos Fuentes' father wants a child because he is happy – in a Mexico that makes people sad. Arundhati Roy's storyteller gives birth to favourite tales and cherishes them like unruly children, with a hint of adult regret. School and learning are a source of joy for Njoroge in the story from Kenya by Ngũgĩ wa Thiong'o – but, like children the world over, he is tormented by the cruelty of his classmates. Heinz Insu Fenkl has ambiguous feelings, too, about a new arrival in South Korea – will they be friends or rivals? A child in Malaysia opens Cecil Rajendra's eyes. Olive Senior gets breathless as she relates the joy of a stay with grandmother in Jamaica.

MEXICO IS A COUNTRY OF SAD MEN and happy children,' said my father, Angel (twenty-four years old), at the instant of my creation.

Before that, my mother, Angeles (under thirty), had sighed: 'Ocean, origin of the gods.'

'But soon there shall be no time for happiness, and we shall all be sad, old and young alike,' my father went on, taking off his glasses – tinted violet, gold-framed, utterly John Lennonish.

'Why do you want a child, then?' my mother said, sighing again.

'Because soon there will be no time for happiness.'

'Was there ever such a time?'

'What did you say? Things turn out badly in Mexico.'

'Don't be redundant. Mexico was *made* so things could turn out badly.'

So she insisted: 'Why do you want a child, then?'

'Because *I* am happy,' my father bellowed. '*I am happy!*' he shouted even louder, turning to face the Pacific Ocean. 'I am possessed of the most intimate, reactionary happiness!'

Ocean, origin of the gods! And she took her copy of Plato's *Dialogues*, the edition published in the twenties by Don José Vasconcelos, when he was the rector of the University of Mexico, and put it over her face. The green covers bearing the black seal of the university and its motto, THROUGH MY RACE SHALL SPEAK THE SPIRIT, were stained with Coppertonic sweat.

But my father said he wanted to sire a son (me, zero years), right here while they were vacationing in Acapulco, 'in front of the ocean, origin of the gods?' quoth Homerica Vespussy. So my naked father crawled across the beach, feeling the hot sand drifting between his legs but saying that sex is not between the legs but inside the coconut grove, around the svelte, naked, innocent body of my mother with the volume of Plato draped over her face, Mom and Dad naked under the blazing and drunken sun of Acapulco on the day they invented me. Gracias, gracias, Mom and Dad.

from **CHRISTOPHER UNBORN** by Carlos Fuentes, Mexico

/ TAXI /

Taking the family Beetle on holiday in Mexico City. Choking fumes mean that most taxis have now been painted green and switched to unleaded fuel, but it's still not enough and children grow up in the world's largest city inhaling the world's worst pollution.

Photo: Amadeo Vergani

IN THE BROAD, COVERED CORRIDOR – the colonnaded kuthambalam abutting the heart of the temple where the Blue God lived with his flute, the drummers drummed and the dancers danced, their colours turning slowly in the night. Rahel sat down cross-legged, resting her back against the roundness of a white pillar. A tall canister of coconut oil gleamed in the flickering light of the brass lamp. The oil replenished the light. The light lit the tin.

It didn't matter that the story had begun, because kathakali discovered long ago that the secret of the Great Stories is that they *have* no secrets. The Great Stories are the ones you have heard and want to hear again. The ones you can enter anywhere and inhabit comfortably. They don't deceive you with thrills and trick endings. They don't surprise you with the unforeseen. They are as familiar as the house you live in. Or the smell of your lover's skin. You know how they end, yet you listen as though you don't. In the way that although you know that one day you will die, you live as though you won't. In the Great Stories you know who lives, who dies, who finds love, who doesn't. And yet you want to know again.

That is their mystery and their magic.

a rakshasa with a new idea into a gossipy Malayali with a scanda spread. From the sensuousness of a woman with a baby at her br into the seductive mischief of Krishna's smile. He can reveal nugget of sorrow that happiness contains. The hidden fish of sham a sea of glory.

He tells stories of the gods, but his yarn is spun from the ungo human heart.

The Kathakali Man is the most beautiful of men. Because his bod his soul. His only instrument. From the age of three it has been pla and polished, pared down, harnessed wholly to the task of st telling. He has magic in him, this man within the painted mask swirling skirts.

But these days he has become unviable. Unfeasible. Condem goods. His children deride him. They long to be everything he is He has watched them grow up to become clerks and bus conduct Class IV non-gazetted officers. With unions of their own.

But he himself, left dangling somewhere between heaven and ea cannot do what they do. He cannot slide down the aisles of bu counting change and selling tickets. He cannot answer bells that s

ON MONDAY, NJOROGE went to school. He did not quite know where it was. He had never gone there, though he knew the direction to it. Mwihaki took him and showed him the way. Mwihaki was a young girl. Njoroge had always admired her. Once some herd-boys had quarrelled with Mwihaki's brothers. They had thrown stones and one had struck her. Then the boys had run away, followed by her brothers. She had been left alone crying. Njoroge, who had been watching the scene from a distance, now approached and felt like soothing the weeping child. Now she, the more experienced, was taking him to school.

Mwihaki was a daughter of Jacobo. Jacobo owned the land on which Ngotho lived. Ngotho was a *Muhoi*. Njoroge had never come to understand how his father had become a *Muhoi*. Maybe a child did not know such matters. They were too deep for him. Jacobo had small boys and one big son and big daughter. The big daughter was a teacher. Her name was Lucia. Njoroge always thought Lucia a nice name. And his sisters had ugly names. Not like Lucia.

The other boys were rough. They laughed at him and made coarse jokes that shocked him. His former high regard of schoolboys was shaken. He thought that he would never like to make such jokes. Nyokabi, his mother, would be angry if he did.

One boy told him, 'You are a *Njuka*.'

'No! I am not a *Nju-u-uka*,' he said.

'What are you?'

'I am Njoroge'

They laughed heartily. He felt annoyed. Had he said anything funny? Another boy commanded him, 'Carry this bag. You're a *Njuka*.'

He was going to take it. But Mwihaki came to his rescue.

'He is my *Njuka*. You cannot touch him.' Some laughed. Others sneered.

'Leave Mwihaki's *Njuka* alone.'

'He is Mwihaki's boy.'

'He'll make a good husband. A *Njuka* is to be a husband of Mwihaki.'

'A *Njuka* is a *Njuka*. He must carry my bag for me.'

All this talk embarrassed and confused Njoroge. He did not know what to do. Mwihaki was annoyed. She burst out: 'Yes, he is my *Njuka*. Let any of you touch him.'

Silence followed. Njoroge was grateful. Apparently the boys feared her because her sister was a teacher and Mwihaki might report them.

The school looked a strange place. But fascinating. The church, huge and hollow, attracted him. It looked haunted. He knew it was the House of God. But some boys shouted while they were in there. This too shocked him. He had been brought up to respect all holy places, like graveyards and the bush around fig trees.

The teacher wore a white blouse and a green skirt. Njoroge liked the white and green because it was like a blooming white flower on a green plant. Grass in this country was green in wet weather and flowers bloomed white all over the land, especially in Njahi season. Njoroge, however, feared her when two days later she beat a boy, whack! whack! ('Bring the other hand') whack! whack! whack! The stick broke into bits. Njoroge could almost feel the pain. It was as if it was being communicated to him without physical contact. The teacher looked ugly while she punished. Njoroge hated seeing anybody being thrashed and he was sorry for the boy. But he should not have bullied a *Njuka*. It was on that day that Njoroge learnt that *Njuka* was the name given to a newcomer. ◼

from **WEEP NOT, CHILD** by Ngũgĩ wa Thiong'o, Kenya

Schoolboys from Lamu on the coast of Kenya, where there is a strong Islamic influence. The area receives Saudi Arabian aid for schools, hospitals and religious centres.

Photo: Piers Cavendish/ Impact Photo Agency

IT WAS THE FIRST and in retrospect also the last time that my mother missed work to be with me. But neither she nor her mother, who also returned, hugged me. They stared at me and stayed with me and I dried up. They even made me crack under the abundance of their glow. That they wondered in the meantime what could be done to keep the rainy season out of the house was about as meaningful as my stubborn silence. My thoughts came together as lines, so that I saw squares everywhere in which the faces of children appeared like billions of light points, so illuminated by the sun that my tears stiffened to crystals on their skins. Another crying fit. Another flood of tears.

'Why do you cry?'
'Ask the rain.'
'What should we do for you.'
'Wait – wait till it's over – over.'

Of course they saw another storm coming when the housekeeper held me against her skin and hummed the melodies of the popular songs she had sung in my preschool years: *Perun Perun mi patron san' wani kon' mak' a kon' Ingrisisma sa t jar' na planga go na Jobopan ala den grikibi den no sabi na fin' fin' wroka Kodjo Kodjo fa ju mofo langa so pur wan'* –
Even if this was the first time I could not laugh – I put my arms around her and I pressed my face deeper in her neck and I allowed the sound of my pain to come out with her so that I knew once and for all that, even after years of distance, nothing had come between us except the sort of knowledge that makes a difference.

The other two women, however, did not really stop to think about the full implications of the occasion. Not even interrupted by my sniffing – perhaps accompanied by the humming – they emptied the housekeeper's shopping bags. As in a rhythmic shift of image my grandmother bends to the floor and with her arm stretched she hands her daughter something ripe, something green, something wrapped. I get the urge to be even louder, not even to get their attention but to demand their skin. I get the idea of dying on the spot, not to receive their mourning but to demand their care. I would lie in state and they would kiss me repeatedly from head to toe – their fingertips would caress my skin in its most naked folds – they would cleanse my organs in palm-wine spiced with myrrh and cinnamon – they would wash my cavities with cedar oil – they would wrap me in hot Zanderij sand to dehydrate me – they would soak metres of linen in resin – they would cut the purple wood from the purpleheart tree for my coffin they would pierce the soil of Albina to paint my face with minerals. Preserved by their care I would live on with artificial eyes that could resist especially the desire to die in my mother's arms. God, I should not have given in to this wishdream which was so charged that the housekeeper's body started to tremble – more and more strongly, as if the rhythm of my heart was imposing itself on her to turn her briefly into a messenger. ■

from **A NAME FOR LOVE** by Astrid Roemer, Surinam

In the tropical forests of Surinam you can take a shower by stepping out into the rain. No-one bothers to protect themselves. These two brothers from one of the dozens of indigenous groups in the region have lived with the rains all their lives, but that doesn't dull their enjoyment.

Photo: Andrew Forrest/ Environmental Picture Library

I KNOW THAT MY FATHER had wished for another son; I remember, because the name he had picked was 'Helmut' – helmet – a name that would have been even more terrible than mine in a schoolyard full of English-speaking military brats. I had secretly wished for a boy as well, but when Anna fell into this world I knew that she had willed herself into being, that nothing could have changed her from being anything but herself.

Because she had lingered so long in my mother's womb, Anna was heavier and larger than I had been at birth. But she was also denser, as if she existed fiercely, as if she were so much realer than other things that her flesh had assumed a substance of stone.

They say the oldest child is jealous of younger siblings, that the relationship is a mixture of love and hate. I did not hate my younger sister, and I was not jealous of her. I think I loved her at first the way a child will innocently love an infant – it is the most natural thing to do. But if I had to describe, in a word, how I felt toward her afterward I would say that I respected her. She learned to speak much later than I had, so late that we might have believed her mute if not for the frightening knowledge in her eyes. Until she spoke, her eyes were an unearthly bottle green, and I knew with the certainty that only children possess that she could see into the other world. Like those fated to be great Buddhist masters, she had been born with memories of her previous lives and a vision that cut both forward and backward through time. When she looked at me as she sucked on her bottle of Similac, one hand worrying her hair, she saw me as an infant, an old man, a brother, a stranger. She smiled at things the rest of us could not see or turned her head attentively toward things we could not hear. When she finally spoke, she would always call me her 'little' older brother no matter how many times we all corrected her. ▪

from **MEMORIES OF MY GHOST BROTHER** by Heinz Insu Fenkl, South Korea

Celebrating the birth of Buddha on the streets of downtown Seoul, South Korea. As dusk falls, rows of lanterns are lit, worshippers murmur prayers, each with a tag bearing family names. In Korea the swastika is an untainted ancient symbol of the Buddha.

Photo: Paul van Riel

SINCE YOU CAME
your eyes
have awakened mine
taught them to see

Never knew
such magic
in a simple blade
of grass
such laughter
in the crackle of a
newspaper
such horror
in a single departure

With you
everything's wonder
adventure
a door knob, a gear
the contents of a bin
a red umbrella
reflections in a mirror
bubbles dancing on water

I shall never again
be bored, be lonely
learning as you do
to converse not only
with dog, flower, tree
but also with calendar
powderpuff & safety-pin
an old bit of string
a bunch of jangling keys.

You have taught me
joy, intensity
curiosity
terror, adventure
laughter
You have shattered
complacency
Since you came
my life
has been touched
by yours
my eyes awakened
by yours
before you came
they were only
open
couldn't really see.

from **BROKEN BUDS** by Cecil Rajendra, Malaysia

Grandfather Lawe
Padan is a big noise
in the village of Pa
Dalih, Malaysia, but
he lives in the same
longhouse as his
granddaughter and so
they can find joy in
each other every day.

Photo:
Sally & Richard Greenhill

MUMMY, YOU KNOW WHAT? Grandma Del has baby chickens. Yellow and white ones. She makes me hold them. And I help her gather eggs but I don't like to go out the back alone because the turkey gobbler goes gobble! gobble! gobble! after my legs, he scares me and Mr SonSon next door has baby pigs I don't like the mother pig though. Grandma lives in this pretty little house with white lace curtains at all the windows, Mummy you must come with me and Daddy next time and you can peek through the louvres Grandma calls them jalousies isn't that funny and you can see the people passing by. But they can't see you. Mummy why can't we have lace curtains like Grandma Del so we can peek through nobody ever goes by our house except the gardeners and the maids and people begging and Rastas selling brooms. Many many people go by Grandma Del's house and they all call out to her and Grandma Del knows everyone. My special friend is Miss Princess the postmistress who plays the organ in church she wears tight shiny dresses and her hair piled so on her head and she walks very slow and everybody says she is sweet on Mr Blake who is the new teacher and he takes the service in church when Parson doesn't come and Miss Princess gets so nervous she mixes up all the hymns. Mr Mack came to fix Grandma's roof and Grandma said 'poorman poorman' all the time. Mr Mack's daughters Eulalie and Ermandine are big girls at high school in town though Eulalie fell and they don't know what is to be done. Mummy, why are they so worried that Eulalie fell? She didn't break her leg or anything like that for she is walking up and down past the house all day long and looks perfectly fine to me.

Mummy, I really like Grandma Del's house it's nice and cosy and dark and cool inside with these big lovely oval picture frames of her family and Daddy as a baby and Daddy as a little boy and Daddy on the high school football team, they won Manning Cup that year Grandma says did you know that Mummy? And Daddy at University and a wedding picture of Daddy and you and me as a baby and all the pictures you send Grandma every year but those are the small pictures on the side table with the lovely white lace tablecloth in the picture frame on the wall is Great-grandpapa Del with a long beard and whiskers he makes me giggle and he is sitting down in a chair and Great-grandmama is standing behind him and then there is a picture of Grandma herself as a young lady with her hair piled high like Miss Princess and her legs crossed at the ankles she looks so lovely. But you know what, Mummy,

I didn't see a picture of Daddy's father and when I asked Grandma she got mad and shooed me away. She gets even madder when I asked her to show me her wedding picture. I only want to see it.

Mummy, you know that Grandma sends me to Sunday School? And then we stay over for the big church and then I walk home with her and all the people it's so nice and only Parson comes to church in a car. Mummy did you go to Sunday School? I go with Joycie a big girl next door and Grandma made me three dresses to wear. She says she cannot imagine how a girl-child (that's me) can leave her home with nothing but blue jeans and T-shirts and shorts and not a single church dress. She has this funny sewing machine, not like Aunt Thelma's, she has to use her feet to make it go just like the organ in church Miss Princess pumps away with her feet to make it give out this lovely sound she works so hard you should see her and the first time I went to Grandma's church I was so scared of the bats! The church is full of bats but usually they stay high up in the roof but as soon as the organ starts playing on Sunday the bats start swooping lower and lower and one swooped so low I nearly died of fright and clutched Grandma Del so tight my hat flew off.

Did I tell you Grandma made me a hat to go to church with her own two hands? She pulled apart one of her old straw hats, leghorn she said, and made me a little hat that fits just so on my head with a bunch of tiny pink flowers. Grandma didn't send it with me though or my Sunday dresses she says she will keep them till I return for she knows that I am growing heathenish in town. When Grandma dresses me up for church I feel so beautiful in my dresses she made with lace and bows and little tucks so beautiful and my hat, I feel so special that my own Grandma made these for me with her own two hands and didn't buy them in a store. Grandma loves to comb my hair she says it's so long and thick and she rubs it with castor oil every night. I hate the smell of castor oil but she says it's the best thing for hair to make it thick and soft and after a little I even like the smell. Grandma Del says my skin is beautiful like honey and all in all I am a fine brown lady and must make sure to grow as beautiful inside as I am outside but Mummy how do I go about doing that?

Nights at Grandma's are very funny. Mummy can you imagine there's no TV? And it's very, very dark. No street lights or any lights and we go to bed so early and every night Grandma lights the oil lamps and then we blow them out when we are going to bed, you have to take →

Religious traditions – and their physical and moral trappings – live on in the Caribbean island of Grenada.

Photo: Amadeo Vergani

a deep breath and every morning Grandma checks the oil in the lamps and cleans the shades. They have 'Home Sweet Home' written all around them. So beautiful. She cleans the shades with newspapers. She says when I come next year I'll be old enough to clean the shades all by myself Grandma knows such lovely stories; she tells me stories every night not stories from a book you know, Mummy, the way you read to me, but stories straight from her head. Really! I am going to learn stories from Grandma so when I am a grown lady I will remember all these stories to tell my children. Mummy, do you think I will?

Mummy, you know Grandma Elaine is so funny she says I'm not to call her Grandma any more, I'm to call her Towser like everybody else for I'm growing so fast nobody would believe that she could have such a big young lady for a grandmother. I think it's funny I'm practising calling her Towser, Grandma Del introduces me to everyone as her Granddaughter she calls me her 'little gran' and Grandma Elaine says, 'Darling, the way your Grandmother Del looks and conducts herself she couldn't be anything but a Grandmother and honey she and I are of entirely different generations.'

Grandma Elaine says such funny things sometimes. Like she was dressing to go out last night and she was putting on make-up and I said 'Grandma' – she was still Grandma then – I said 'Grandma, you shouldn't paint your face like you know, it is written in the Bible that it's a sin. Grandma Del says so and I will never paint my face.' And she said, 'Darling, with all due respect to your paternal Grandmother, she's a lovely lady or was when I met her the one and only time at the wedding, and she has done one absolutely fantastic thing in her life which is to produce one son, your esteemed father, one hunk of a guy, but honey, other than that your Grandmother Del is a country bumpkin of the deepest waters and don't quote her goddamn sayings to me.' Mummy, you know Grandma Elaine swears like that all the time? I said, 'Grandma you mustn't swear and take the name of the Lord in vain.' And she said, 'Honeychile with all due respect to the grey hairs of your old grandmother and the first-class brainwashing your daddy is allowing her to give you, I wish my granddaughter would get off my back and leave me to go to Hell in peace.' Can you imagine she said that?

She's really mad that you allow me to spend time with Grandma Del. She says, 'Honey, I really don't know what your mother thinks she is doing making you spend so much time down there in the deepest darkest country. I really must take you in hand. It's embarrassing to hear some of the things you come out with sometimes. Your mother would be better advised to send you to Charm School next summer you are never too young to start. Melody-Ann next door went last year and it's done wonders for her, turned her from a tomboy into a real little lady.' (though Mummy, I really can't stand Melody-Ann any more, you know) 'And your mother had better start to do something about your hair from now it's almost as tough as your father's and I warned your mother about it from the very start I said "Honey, love's alright but what about the children's hair?" If you were my child I would cut it right off to get some of the kinks out.' Mummy, you won't cut off my hair, will you? Daddy and Grandma Del like it just the way it is and what does Grandma Elaine mean when she says my hair is tough, Mummy?

from **THE TWO GRANDMOTHERS** by Olive Senior, Jamaica

joy and sorrow

dreams and nightmares

WHEN FIRST WE FALL ASLEEP we can't be sure if friendly ghosts or angry ghouls will visit us. Impoverished and hungry, the Bolivian kids remembered by Domitila Barrios de Chungara dream of doing good – and of one day being able to give food to the hungry. In the treacherous South Pacific Ocean the great white shark steals in, not for the kill, but to the rescue of Sitiveni Kalouniviti's stranded child. Eduardo Galeano finds his childhood daydreams of soccer stardom crashing to the solid earth of middle age – not unlike the soccer stars themselves. The indigenous children of the Amazon take flight from hunger to form the stars in a poignant myth translated by Christopher Hampton. Ben Okri summons up ancestral spirits who wonder at how little we have learned, while Suniti Namjoshi looks a fearful dragon in the eye – and terror melts into strangeness.

SOMETIMES WE WENT HUNGRY and there wasn't enough food, since my father could only afford a little. When you're small, it's hard to live in poverty and with all kinds of problems. But that developed something strong in us; a great sensitivity, a great desire to help all the people. Our children's games always had something to do with our kind of life and with how we wanted to live. Also, during our childhood we'd seen that even though we didn't have much, my mother and father were always helping different families in Pulacayo. So when we saw poor people begging in the street, me and my sisters would start dreaming. We'd dream that one day we'd be big, that we'd have land, that we'd plant, and that we'd give those poor people food. And any time we had a little sugar or coffee or something else left over, and we heard a sound, we'd say: 'A poor person's passing by. Look, here's a little rice, a little sugar.' And we'd wrap it up in a rag and throw it out into the street for some poor person to pick up.

Once we threw out some coffee when my father was coming back from work. And when he came into the house he really scolded us and said: 'How can you waste the little that we have? How can you throw out what costs me so much to earn for you?' And he really beat us. But those things were things that just occurred to us, we thought that that way we would help someone, see?

from **LET ME SPEAK!** by Domitila Barrios de Chungara, Bolivia

A young girl at the side of a mountain road in Bolivia sells refreshments while keeping an eye on her younger brother and sister. Her small earnings contribute to the family income.

Photo: Kathrin Buechler

IT WAS ONE OF THOSE DAYS when even the wind co-operated with the clouds of the sky to create a romantic atmosphere typical of Nadi village. The bay below glittered in the sunlight. Everything was peaceful. The palms waved silvery on the beach and danced to the murmur of the wind. The only sound came from the train-like rolls of the waves on the reef, a good half-mile from the shore. The white foam of the waves raced across the mouth of the bay in a delightful cavalry charge, only to be shattered into grand displays of rainbow colours and silvery clouds of sea-spray by the great rock, Na vatu levu, which guards the entrance to Nadi Bay.

I was sitting on the doorstep of our kitchen, wishing I was out there on the bay, fishing. I often heard of Tai's adventures out in that bay and my heart longed for a chance to prove that I no longer needed my parents' care. I wanted to be like Tai. The booming of the waves breaking on that reef always created in me a feeling of excitement. Many a time my dreams drove me to the point of running away to the shore, but my parents usually found out and these misdeeds, as they called them, often resulted in very savage beatings. I could not find out how they knew about my actions. It was probably that they were so obvious. Sometimes I was ordered not to go near that shore even before I told them anything about it.

My longings stayed with me and often haunted me in my dreams at night. I found myself lonely as ever since my friends spent most of their time at sea. In the evenings they usually flocked around me in our kitchen and noisily told me how they fished with their lines and spears. Oftentimes these story sessions resulted in quarrels when my friends found that their stories conflicted.

To make up for the loss, I made myself a spear using the framework of an old umbrella. The steel frames, after being sharpened by a file, were tightly fastened by old pieces of wire to the end of a bamboo-like reed, about two yards in length. I wandered around the village with this spear and even slept with it tucked under my mat. At such times I took great care not to roll on it lest I should bend the spikes.

My desire to prove myself as a fisherman could only be fulfilled in the brook nearby. Most of my time was spent in this brook with my imagination changing it into a sea of my own. The gurgling of the cool fresh water over the round, tiny pebbles became great sea waves crashing on the reef. Tiny prawns suddenly sprang up as huge monsters that I had to save the village from.

I tried on several occasions to create a pool in which I could nurse my small prawns and tiny fish, but the barriers I made of clay and coconut shells were usually washed away, if they were not trodden upon by the village bullocks which used the brook as a drinking place. At one stage, I succeeded in rolling a coconut stem into place across the brook and this created a large pool which enabled me to stand waist deep in it. Next morning, however, to my dismay, I found that the coconut stem had been washed away.

Thus were my longings fulfilled. Sometimes I went to the extreme and toads became unfortunate victims of my worthless dreams. I was still far from being satisfied. The thunderous roar of the waves out on the reef continued to have its effect on me.

My respect for the bay was mingled with a certain amount of fear. It had lived in me ever since I was old enough to reason out the stories that my elders told me. Tai's exploits in Nadi Bay were well known throughout the district. One day he told me that to fish one had to be gifted with the craft of the sea, for to sail beyond those reefs in a canoe required great skill and courage. He also told me that the help of guardian spirits was required, and the Great White Shark of Nadi Bay was a wonderful helper in times of distress. This I could believe. I had heard of many times when the shark had led canoes through the reef passage in bad weather.

In one case – which I would have witnessed myself if Nau had not chased me home – the whole village saw the white shark in action. The women, in preparation for a feast, went down to the bay for a mass fishing occasion. They used large nets dropped at one end of the bay, then started rowing towards the entrance to make enough noise to drive the fish into the nets. They had hardly reached half-way when they saw the greatest disturbance of water they had ever witnessed. Amid the spray and foam they made out a huge white fin, rushing from side to side. The great white guardian of Nadi Bay was in action again.

They could see that the shark was deliberately chasing fish towards the nets, its tail smacking the water with frightening thunderclaps. Retreating behind the nets, the villagers hauled in the fish as the shark held down the bottom of the net so that no fish could escape. When they had enough fish for the occasion, the villagers tenderly pulled up the heavy nets and pushed the shark back into the water. After that, all they saw was a display of tail and water, a racing fin which gradually vanished into the blue, silvery distance.

The son of Tuari – who earns his living fishing for tuna in the dangerous ocean beyond the reef off the small town of Taravao in Tahiti – pauses on his way back home at dusk.

Photo: David Ransom/ New Internationalist

My great attraction for the bay was increased by my desire to meet the shark. One day I managed to slip down to the shore, where I strained my eyes in vain, scanning the horizon for a white fin. Finding this was useless, I went knee-deep into the water and tried looking beneath the surface with my eyes. I called out, feebly at first, then yelling to the shark at the top of my voice. But all my efforts were in vain. I walked home with a heavy heart, cursing all the spirits in the world, and myself. The thought that spirits could read my mind set me sprinting up the hill towards the village, fearing to look back.

My big chance came unexpectedly. One morning I was still engrossed in dreams on our kitchen doorstep when Tai came past with his spears. He was my grandfather. He had the most beautiful white hair of all the men in the village. He was tall and slender. His arms were full of tell-tale scars from his encounters with wild boars and deep-water fish. I loved him with all my heart.

'It's a very fine day, isn't it?' he said. 'Very fine indeed. I think we'll have a successful trip today. I hope he's out there, because I know he will bless us again today.' After saying that he started mumbling and chanting to himself. I nodded. There was no hope of my ever going on a trip with him.

'Tai, who are you going with today?' I asked weakly.

'Oh, all the old ones. Old people like fishing together. They have the touch! I think with this weather we should make good catches.'

My hopes – if there were any left – sank. The old men of the village were very fussy about taking children out, especially on fishing trips. They usually regarded us as an extra burden. Tai's eyes were still fixed on the bay below, as if he could see the movements of the fish beneath the water.

'I'm looking for Masi,' he said. 'I need someone to carry my things on the reef. Do you know where he is?'

I tried with all my might to conceal the spur of hope in my voice when I told him Masi was in the garden getting some food for lunch. Tai did not look at me. He was still glancing at something on the reef. Oh, how I wanted to blurt out: 'Take me with you, Tai! Please, please!' I stood there trying to act as uninterested as possible. I tried to whistle, but my lips began to quiver.

It was the call from the other side of the village that made Tai's mind up about me. Masi could not come. So I was to have my first taste of real fishing that day, as Tai's carrier. The heaviness of my task did not matter. I was so excited that the amount of things I had to carry became part of the adventure.

I could feel my heart lift with the waves as the canoe sliced its way towards the reef. In the centre of the bay the water was clear and I could see dark patches of seaweed and bright golden intervals of sand glittering in the sunlight. Everywhere shoals of fish rushed from side to side creating a complex of beautiful colours playing hide-and-seek beneath our canoe. I wondered what life down there would be like and longed to be part of it.

When we reached the reef, the pictures that I had formed on land were shattered by the great beauty of the place. The display of corals of all colours and the variety of vivid fish were far beyond what I had often dreamed. I felt as if I were in another world – a world so beautiful that to take anything away from it would be a mortal sin.

The old men had other interests. They wanted to fish. The sea was heaven for them, too. As I had expected I was completely forgotten. This created an opportunity for exploration. My wanderings along the reef brought me to the great rock. It was about five metres high. It had a flat top and on it were the remnants of fire and fish bones – it was used as a picnic site.

From the top I could see Tai and the others, small shadowy figures who seemed to be floating upright on the surface of the water. I could hear them quite clearly and was surprised that their words could be very rough while they were on a fishing trip. Towards the deeper parts of the entrance I could see great arrays of fish darting around, obviously being frightened by the presence of larger predators. Others did not seem to care. A huge eel glided past. I reasoned that the ones that paid no attention were probably poisonous.

The warmth of the rock, the flickering sunlight and the slight, soothing breeze made me sleepy. The excited shouts of my companions slowly faded away. The only music that clouded my mind was the movement of the wind over the water and the booming of distant waves on the reef. My dreams were wonderful, with all the beautiful things that anyone of my age could possibly imagine: I was the Neptune of our wonderful bay; I made breathtaking discoveries; I was the greatest fisherman of all time.

I was blown out of that wondrous world by a great wave breaking like an explosion not three metres away from the rock. Suddenly it dawned on me. I really was on a trip. Yes, they were all gone, every last one of them. Even Tai had forgotten he had brought me with him. The sun was almost hidden beyond the hills. The tide was coming in rapidly and the day was creeping away into darkness.

I was filled with despair. I could feel a great fear shaping itself at the back of my head. All the stories of this bay, this rock, crept slowly into my mind like painful needles. I felt sweat on the palm of my hands and down my back. I began to shiver, thinking of the oncoming darkness. My mind raced to the village graveyard, the church, my father. Yet there was no way of stopping the cold fear that began to grip the very hairs on my body. The sea turned angry. The murmur of the wind became the whisperings of uncountable ghosts. The rock shuddered, as if it were trying to throw me off into the angry water. Soon there would be darkness and...

My mind went blank and I jumped into the water. I must reach the shore before... My limbs worked flat-out, my tiny muscles competing piteously against the great waves. Gradually my body weakened. I began to realize that I could not fight. Up there on the hill the first light from the village flickered towards the bay. I called out frantically but couldn't hold myself up long enough to see the light again. I was sinking, going down, down, down...

Then, with the moment of oblivion, I felt a searing, scratching pain. I was floating. In front of me was the largest, whitest fin I had ever seen, slicing through the water like the periscope of a nuclear submarine. The shore came rushing towards me. I knew I had to be dreaming. 'Please let me dream on!' I thought. I was roughly tipped over. I found I was able to stand and walk to the shore. I looked across my shoulder and saw a great display of sea-spray, a silvery white tail. The moon was just above the horizon. My body weakened and I collapsed on the sand.

'But he's only seven! And half-a-mile of rough sea is too much for him to swim. And those scratches on his thighs and stomach? It looks as if he's been riding a log. Unless...' Those were the last words I heard before the warmth and softness of my bed engulfed me once more in a world of darkness.

from **A Childhood Experience** in Fiji Writers' Association, by Sitiveni Kalouniviti, Fiji

A CONFESSION

Like all Uruguayan children, I wanted to be a football player. I played quite well, in fact I was terrific, but only at night when I was asleep. During the day I was the worst wooden-leg ever to set foot on the little football fields of my country.

As a fan I also left a lot to be desired. Juan Alberto Schiaffino and Julio Cesar Abbadie played for Pearol, the enemy side. I was a loyal Nacional fan and I did everything I could to hate them. But with his masterful passes 'El Pepe' Schiaffino orchestrated the team's plays as if he were watching from the highest tower in the stadium, and 'El Pardo' Abbadie, running in his seven-league boots, would slide the ball all the way down the white touchline, swaying back and forth without ever grazing the ball or his opponents. I couldn't help admiring them, and I even felt like cheering.

Years have gone by and I've finally learned to accept myself for what I am: I am a mere beggar for good football. I go about the world, hand outstretched, and in the stadiums I plead: 'A pretty move, for the love of God.'

And when good football happens, I give thanks for the miracle and don't give a damn which club or country performs it.

THE IDOL

And one fine day the goddess of the wind kisses the foot of man, that mistreated, scorned foot, and from that kiss the football idol is born. He is born in a straw crib in a tin-roofed shack and he enters the world clinging to a football.

From the moment he learns to walk, he knows how to play. In his early years he brings joy to the empty lots, plays like crazy in the back alleys of the slums until night falls and you can't see the ball, and in his early manhood he takes flight and the stadiums fly with him. His acrobatic art draws multitudes, Sunday after Sunday, from victory to victory, ovation to ovation.

The ball seeks him out, knows him, needs him. She rests and rocks on the top of his foot. He caresses her and makes her speak, and in that tête-a-tête millions of mutes converse. The nobodies, those condemned to always be nobodies, feel they are somebodies for a moment by virtue of those one-two passes, those dribbles tracing Zs on the grass, those incredible backheel goals or overhead volleys. When he plays, the team has twelve players: *'Twelve? It has fifteen! Twenty!'*

The ball laughs, radiant, in the air. He brings her down, puts her to sleep, showers her with compliments, dances with her, and seeing such things never before seen his admirers feel pity for their unborn grandchildren who will never see them.

But the idol is an idol for only a moment, a human eternity, all or nothing; and when the time comes for the golden foot to become a lame duck, the star will have completed his journey from sparkle to blackout. His body has more mends and patches than a clown's suit, and by now the acrobat is a cripple, the artist a beast of burden: *'Not with your clodhoppers!'*

The fountain of public joy becomes the lightning rod of public rancour: *'You dummy!'*

Sometimes the idol doesn't fall at once. And sometimes when he breaks, people devour the pieces.

from **FOOTBALL IN SUN AND SHADOW** by Eduardo Galeano, Uruguay
translated by Mark Fried

There's no wasted space for aspiring footballers in Buenos Aires, Argentina. Streets, parks and wastelands are pressed into service in this football-mad country.

Photo: Julio Etchart

IN THE BEGINNING there was a river. The river became a road and the road branched out to the whole world. And because the road was once a river it was always hungry.

In that land of beginnings, spirits mingled with the unborn. We could assume numerous forms. Many of us were birds. We knew no boundaries. There was much feasting, playing and sorrowing. We feasted much because of the beautiful terrors of eternity. We played much because we were free. And we sorrowed much because there were always those amongst us who had just returned from the world of the Living. They had returned inconsolable for all the love they had left behind, all the suffering they hadn't redeemed, all that they hadn't understood, and for all that they had barely begun to learn before they were drawn back to the land of origins.

There was not one amongst us who looked forward to being born. We disliked the rigours of existence, the unfulfilled longings, the enshrined injustices of the world, the labyrinths of love, the ignorance of parents, the fact of dying, and the amazing indifference of the Living in the midst of the simple beauties of the universe. We feared the heartlessness of human beings, all of whom are born blind, few of whom ever learn to see. ▪

from **THE FAMISHED ROAD** by Ben Okri, Nigeria

The spirit world visits the land of the living in Côte d'Ivoire. Panther men, from a mystic society of the We people, return home after being initiated in the bush.

Photo: M & A Kirtley/ Agence ANA

THE CHILDREN WERE ALWAYS HUNGRY.

Their parents said: 'We give you all we can, why do you complain?'
But the children only cried and said again that they were hungry.
In the ashes of the fire their mother found the jaw-bone
of a tapir and threw it to them.
They took what meat they could from the bone and
divided it among the youngest.
When they saw there was nothing left, they knew that
they would have to leave.
They joined hands, sang a song and climbed slowly up
into the sky.
Their mother said: 'Come back, come back. We will find
more food for you. Forgive us.'
And the children answered: 'There is nothing to forgive.
We know you did what you could. We bear no grudge.'
They said: 'We are better gone. Here we can help you.
Here we can help to lift the darkness from you.'
And they became stars.

translated from an Amazonian indigenous myth, Brazil;
from the stage play **SAVAGES** by Christopher Hampton

This Karaja boy in the
Amazon rainforest of
Brazil has attached
feathers to patterns
of sap on his body.
Without the knowledge
of indigenous peoples,
rainforests are hard
places to find food.

Photo:
Jesco von Puttkamer

SIR SUNITI AND THE FEARFUL DRAGON

She mocks herself.

> She has done her best to cast out pride.

But this gorgeous fear

> (which makes *her* gorgeous)

– was this the Fear she sought to hide?

SHE IMAGINES HERSELF FACING DEATH

If I could face Death unafraid,

then surely I would be a Conquering Maid?

Afterwards she set out to find her fear. It was not a white hart, luring her with beauty, but transparent and fluid. And it did not lead her into a forest among benign trees, but on to rock-hard pavements, crowded with people. And there it took fright. It leaped into her body. Liquid panic slithered through her, invaded the most remote and tiny capillaries. Her eyes turned to glass; she knew that if anyone touched her, their fingers would freeze, or she would freeze. She felt alert and a little sick. But the fear was turning into crystals now. If it crystallised, she would die of it. The fear must be made to mix with her blood, take colour from it.

She made herself breathe. She allowed the fear to flow freely. When at last she was convinced she would continue to live, she looked about her. Fear was home safe. Now who should she hunt? How kill?

'Perhaps fear is unkillable,' she announced ponderously. 'Perhaps it's a mythical and immortal beast.' Perhaps – and with this thought her heart rose – perhaps this quest is a failed quest, and it is not my duty, much less my aim, to attempt to kill it. She glanced at the dragon lying at her feet. And then, in a flash, saw herself standing there, at the foot of the dragon, puzzled and puny. Perhaps fear is only a large animal... Even so, it did not follow that she had to kill it. On the contrary. She stroked the dragon. Nothing happened. Though large and shapeless, it wasn't slimy. Perhaps it was dead? But it was patently absurd that she, as a saint, or even as a woman, should have to climb up its flanks and stick a flag in its body. She would not do it. She could see it was breathing. But perhaps it was dying? Was it her task to end its misery? Would it not be better to allow it to live, to fulfil, so to speak, its own destiny? She patted its sides, the dragon groaned. 'Help me,' it begged.

'Please help me.' She watched aghast. Who was she to help a heaving dragon? She distanced herself, but the dragon had whelped. She found herself wriggling in a welter of babies.

Though the birds and beasts sing

> and Suniti claimed she witnessed
>
> everything

the canny and clever

> could not discover

what the dragon said

> when nobody else
>
> was listening.

Suniti said, 'He heaved and groaned,

> sighed and moaned...'

Suniti said, 'The dragon skin

> collapsed from within.

The dragon died. In his progeny

> he was glorified.'

'And,' she said,

> 'the dragon screamed,

a fearful, final, fluting scream.

> I dreamed he screamed.

Then he died.'

> But they said
>
> Suniti lied.

Suniti shrugged. She had done her best to give evidence, even to the point of open confession; she had not been believed. It happened sometimes. They had said the dragon survived. She had said the dragon died. There was no contradiction. She would bury the truth in a new jingle. Let them dig for it.

No one sober in spring. Pluck each dragon seedling.
Gather them up in a green salad bowl.
They squeak and they shriek, they pule and they howl;
But pat them and pet them, feed them on cake.
Fool the little darlings. Make no mistake.
When the dragons are grown they'll quickly devour
The life in your veins, the bliss in your bower.

The three-eyed gaze of Shiva the Destroyer emerges from behind its massive wooden grill for a week-long festival in Kathmandu, Nepal. Every night a potent beer spills from its mouth and has a small fish in it which is said to bring special luck to the finder.

Photo: Thomas Laird/ TCS Publishing

 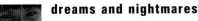

Then stroke them and strike them, kiss them good-bye.
Dragons must sleep if dragons won't die.

With that Suniti staggered to her feet, loaded a syringe and anaesthetised the dragon babies one by one. The effect was instantaneous. They froze without protest and turned into pebbles. It was as though she had managed to freeze-dry them. They could not sprout without careful watering. Concentrating hard she slit her left breast and tucked them away in a waterproof bag.

The she examined her conscience. The deed was done. But had it been well done? A full-grown dragon was in constant danger from passing saints and brave civilians. She had ensured the safety of saints and dragons, also of civilians. A medal was in order. She glanced at the sky, but the tree overhead proffered only apples. She munched an apple. It occurred to her that police and politicians might outrank saints under certain conditions.

THE TRIALS OF THE SAINT

It so happened that as Saint Suniti was walking down the street, absorbed in thoughts concerning the complications of a saintly life, she was suddenly confronted by Grendel and his Mama. The old hag leered at the saint. 'Hey Sunny!' she called. 'We're going to have to eat you, you know. It's not for myself, you understand, but Sonny Boy here is starving to death and I've got to feed him.' Suniti glanced at Grendel, a long adolescent with hungry eyes; she looked away quickly. It was a difficult situation: could she talk her way out?

'Please Madam,' she began tentatively, 'as a fellow woman you are surely unwilling to fatten your son by victimising me?'
'Willing or unwilling, don't really matter,' the Mama replied. 'He's got to be fed and that's about it.' Then she looked cunning, and in a fair imitation of Suniti's voice, added slyly, 'But surely, Sunny, as a fellow woman you ought to be willing to aid and abet?'
Suniti was stumped only for a moment. 'I am,' she replied. 'Come with me and I'll help you to find him something to eat.'
Now as the saint and the mother, with Grendel in tow, stalked the streets, the women ran away or hid in their houses, as did most of the men, though there were one or two who were either too drunk or too brave to take any notice. 'Eat them?' Suniti suggested. Mama glanced at Grendel inquiringly, but Grendel just stood there and looked obstinate. His mouth quivered. It looked as though he was getting ready to howl.
'Poor darling,' his dam explained. 'He has a strong preference for female flesh and he's getting hungry.' She looked at Suniti appraisingly. 'You had better find him something quickly,' she said.

from **SAINT SUNITI AND THE DRAGON** by Suniti Namjoshi, India

work and play

GAMES ARE PLAYED OUT in a vivid childhood world. Anita Desai recreates it — a child sets out in search of the perfect hiding place but discovers something else. Low-wage labour invades childhood all too soon and for all too many children, as Rigoberta Menchú in Guatemala recollects with anger. A swing can turn around the world of Oswald Mbuyisemi Mtshali, while learning and labour conflict head-on in Bangladesh, with cruel results for the girl in the story by Sulekha Sanyal. The exquisite pain of young love ends a celebration of Ecuador's natural wonders by Fanny Carrión de Fierro. Palden Gyatso's train-ing as a monk in Tibet starts early and is strictly enforced, but has its compensations.

IT WAS STILL TOO HOT to play outdoors. They had had their tea, they had been washed and had their hair brushed, and after the long day of confinement in the house that was not cool but at least a protection from the sun, the children strained to get out. Their faces were red and bloated with the effort, but their mother would not open the door, everything was still curtained and shuttered in a way that stifled the children, made them feel that their lungs were stuffed with cotton wool and their noses with dust and if they didn't burst out into the light and see the sun and feel the air, they would choke.

'Please, ma, please,' they begged. 'We'll play in the veranda and porch – we won't go a step out of the porch.'

'You will, you know you will, and then –'

'No – we won't, we won't,' they wailed so horrendously that she actually let down the bolt of the front door so that they burst out like seeds from a crackling, over-ripe pod into the veranda, with such wild, maniacal yells that she retreated to her bath and the shower of talcum powder and the fresh sari that were to help her face the summer evening.

They faced the afternoon. It was too hot. Too bright. The white walls of the veranda glared stridently in the sun. The bougainvillea hung about it, purple and magenta, in livid balloons. The garden outside was like a tray made out of beaten brass, flattened out on the red gravel and the stoney soil in all shades of metal – aluminium, tin, copper, and brass. No life stirred at this arid time of day – the birds still drooped, like dead fruit, in the papery tents of the trees; some squirrels lay limp on the wet earth under the garden tap. The outdoor dog lay stretched as if dead on the veranda mat, his paws and ears and tail all reaching out like dying travellers in search of water. He rolled his eyes at the children – two white marbles rolling in the purple sockets, begging for sympathy – and attempted to lift his tail in a wag but could not. It only twitched and lay still.

Then, perhaps roused by the shrieks of the children, a band of parrots suddenly fell out of the eucalyptus tree, tumbled frantically in the still, sizzling air, then sorted themselves out into battle formation and streaked away across the white sky.

The children, too, felt released. They too began tumbling, shoving, pushing against each other, frantic to start. Start what? Start their business. The business of the children's day which is – play.

'Let's play hide-and-seek.'

'Who'll be It?'

'You be It.'

'Why should I? You be –'

'You're the eldest –'

'That doesn't mean –'

The shoves became harder. Some kicked out. The motherly Mira intervened. She pulled the boys roughly apart. There was a tearing sound of cloth but it was lost in the heavy panting and angry grumbling and no one paid attention to the small sleeve hanging loosely off a shoulder.

'Make a circle, make a circle!' she shouted, firmly pulling and pushing until a kind of vague circle was formed. 'Now clap!' she roared and, clapping, they all chanted in melancholy unison: 'Dip, dip, dip – my blue ship –' and every now and then one or the other saw he was safe by the way his hands fell at the crucial moment – palm on palm, or back of hand on palm – and dropped out of the circle with a yell and a jump of relief and jubilation.

Raghu was It. He started to protest, to cry 'You cheated – Mira cheated – Anu cheated –' but it was too late, the others had already streaked away. There was no one to hear when he called out, 'Only in the veranda – the porch – Ma said – Ma said to stay in the porch!' No one had stopped to listen, all he saw were their brown legs flashing through the dusty shrubs, scrambling up brick walls, leaping over compost heaps and hedges, and then the porch stood empty in the purple shade of the bouganvillea and the garden was as empty as before; even the limp squirrels had whisked away, leaving everything gleaming, brassy and bare.

Only small Manu suddenly reappeared, as if he had dropped out of an invisible cloud or from a bird's claw, and stood for a moment in the centre of the yellow lawn, chewing his finger and near to tears as he heard Raghu shouting, with his head pressed against the veranda wall, 'Eighty-three, eighty-five, eighty-nine, ninety...' and then made off in a panic, half of him wanted to fly north, the other half counselling south. Raghu turned just in time to see the flash of his white shorts and the uncertain skittering of his red sandals, and charged after him with such a blood-curdling yell that Manu stumbled over the hosepipe, fell into its rubber coils and lay there weeping, 'I won't be It – you have to find them all – all – All!'

Carefree in the land of avalanches, which happen regularly in the Ligti valley of Himachal Pradesh, India. Ki-Klooster, the highest village in the world, is nearby.

Photo: Ivo Hendrikx

'I know I have to, idiot,' Raghu said, superciliously kicking him with his toe. 'You're dead,' he said with satisfaction, licking the beads of perspiration off his upper lip, and then stalked off in search of worthier prey, whistling spiritedly so that the hiders should hear and tremble.

Ravi heard the whistling and picked his nose in a panic, trying to find comfort by burrowing the finger deep – deep into that soft tunnel. He felt himself too exposed, sitting on an upturned flower pot behind the garage. Where could he burrow? He could run around the garage if he heard Raghu come – around and around and around – but he hadn't much faith in his short legs when matched against Raghu's long, hefty, hairy footballer legs. Ravi had a frightening glimpse of them as Raghu combed the hedge of crotons and hibiscus, trampling delicate ferns underfoot as he did so. Ravi looked about him desperately, swallowing a small ball of snot in his fear.

The garage was locked with a great heavy lock to which the driver had the key in his room, hanging from a nail on the wall under his workshirt. Ravi had peeped in and seen him sprawling on his string-cot in his vest and striped underpants, the hair on his chest and the hair in his nose shaking with the vibrations of his phlegm–obstructed snores. Ravi had wished he were tall enough, big enough to reach the key on the nail, but it was impossible, beyond his reach for years to come. He had sidled away and sat dejectedly on the flower pot. That at least was cut to his own size.

But next to the garage was another shed with a big green door. Also locked. No one even knew who had the key to the lock. That shed wasn't opened more than once a year when Ma turned out all the old broken bits of furniture and rolls of matting and leaking buckets, and the white ant hills were broken and swept away and Flit sprayed into the spider webs and rat holes so that the whole operation was like the looting of a poor, ruined and conquered city. The green leaves of the door sagged. They were nearly off their rusty hinges. The hinges were large and made a small gap between the door and the walls – only just large enough for rats, dogs and, possibly, Ravi to slip through.

Ravi had never cared to enter such a dark and depressing mortuary of defunct household goods seething with such unspeakable and alarming animal life but, as Raghu's whistling grew angrier and sharper and his crashing and storming in the hedge wilder, Ravi suddenly slipped off the flower pot and through the crack and was gone. He chuckled aloud with astonishment at his own temerity so that Raghu came out of the hedge, stood silent with his hands on his hips, listening, and finally shouted 'I heard you! I'm coming! *Got* you –' and came charging round the garage only to find the upturned flower pot, the yellow dust, the crawling of white ants in a mud-hill against the closed shed door – nothing. Snarling, he bent to pick up a stick and went off, whacking it against the garage and shed walls as if to beat out his prey.

Ravi shook, then shivered with delight, with self-congratulation. Also with fear. It was dark, spooky in the shed. It had a muffled smell, as of graves. Ravi had once got locked into the linen cupboard and sat there weeping for half an hour before he was rescued. But at least that had been a familiar place, and even smelt pleasantly of starch, laundry and, reassuringly, of his mother. But the shed smelt of rats, ant hills, dust and spider webs. Also of less definable, less recognizable horrors. And it was dark. Except for the white-hot cracks along the door, there was no light. The roof was very low. Although Ravi was small, he felt as if he could reach up and touch it with his finger tips. But he didn't stretch. He hunched himself into a ball so as not to bump into anything, touch or feel anything. What might there not be to touch him and feel him as he stood there, trying to see in the dark? Something cold, or slimy – like a snake. Snakes! He leapt up as Raghu whacked the wall with his stick – then, quickly realizing what it was, felt almost relieved to hear Raghu, hear his stick. It made him feel protected.

But Raghu soon moved away. There wasn't a sound once his footsteps had gone around the garage and disappeared. Ravi stood frozen inside the shed. Then he shivered all over. Something had tickled the back of his neck. It took him a while to pick up the courage to lift his hand and explore. It was an insect – perhaps a spider – exploring him. He squashed it and wondered how many more creatures were watching him, waiting to reach out and touch him, the stranger.

There was nothing now. After standing in that position – his hand still on his neck, feeling the wet splodge of his squashed spider gradually dry – for minutes, hours, his legs began to tremble with the effort, the inaction. By now he could see enough in the dark to make out the large solid shapes of old wardrobes, broken buckets and bedsteads piled on top of each other around him. He recognized an old bathtub – patches of enamel glimmered at him and at last he lowered himself onto its edge.

He contemplated slipping out of the shed and into the fray. He wondered if it would not be better to be captured by Raghu and be returned to the milling crowd as long as he could be in the sun, the light, the free spaces of the garden and the familiarity of his brothers, sisters and cousins. It would be evening soon. Their games would become legitimate. The parents would sit out on the lawn on cane basket chairs and watch them as they tore around the garden or gathered in knots to share a loot of mulberries or black, teeth-splitting jamun from the garden trees. The gardener would fix the hosepipe to the water tap and water would fall lavishly through the air to the ground, soaking the dry yellow grass and the red gravel and arousing the sweet, the intoxicating scent of water on dry earth – that loveliest scent in the world. Ravi sniffed for a whiff of it. He half-rose from the bathtub, then heard the despairing scream of one of the girls as Raghu bore down upon her. There was a sound of a crash, and of rolling about in the bushes, the shrubs, then screams and accusing sobs of, 'I touched the den –' 'You did not –' 'I did –' 'You liar, you did not' and then a fading away and silence again.

Ravi sat back on the harsh end of the tub, deciding to hold out a bit longer. What fun if they were all found out and caught – he alone left unconquered! He had never known that sensation. Nothing more wonderful had ever happened to him than being taken out by an uncle and bought a whole slab of chocolate all to himself, or being flung into the soda-man's pony cart and driven up to the gate by the friendly driver with the red beard and pointed ears. To defeat Raghu – that hirsute, hoarse-voiced football champion – and to be the winner in a circle of older, bigger, luckier children – that would be thrilling beyond imagination. He hugged his knees together and smiled to himself almost shyly at the thought of so much victory, such laurels.

There he sat smiling, knocking his heels against the bathtub, now and then getting up and going to the door to put his ear to the broad crack and listening for sounds of the game, the pursuer and the pursued, and then returning to his seat with the dogged determination of the true winner, a breaker of records, a champion.

It grew darker in the shed as the light at the door grew softer, fuzzier, turned to a kind of crumbling yellow pollen that turned to yellow fur, blue fur, grey fur. Evening. Twilight. The sound of water gushing, falling. The scent of earth receiving water, slaking its thirst in great gulps and releasing that green scent of freshness, coolness. Through the crack Ravi saw the long purple shadows of the shed and the garage lying still across the yard. Beyond that, the white walls of the house. The bougainvillea had lost its lividity, hung in dark bundles that quaked and twittered and seethed with masses of homing sparrows. The lawn was shut off from his view. Could he hear the children's voices? It seemed to him that he could. It seemed to him that he could hear them chanting, singing, laughing. But what about the game? What had happened? Could it be over? How could it when he was still not found?

It then occurred to him that he could have slipped out long ago, dashed across the yard to the veranda and touched the 'den'. It was necessary to do that to win. He had forgotten. He had only remembered the part of hiding and trying to elude the seeker. He had done that so successfully, his success had occupied him so wholly that he had quite forgotten that success had to be clinched by that final dash to victory and the ringing cry of 'Den!'

With a whimper he burst through the crack, fell on his knees, got up and stumbled on stiff, benumbed legs across the shadowy yard, crying heartily by the time he reached the veranda so that when he flung himself at the white pillar and bawled, 'Den! Den! Den!' his voice broke with rage and pity at the disgrace of it all and he felt himself flooded with tears and misery.

Out on the lawn, the children stopped chanting. They all turned to stare at him in amazement. Their faces were pale and triangular in the dusk. The trees and bushes around them stood inky and sepulchral, spilling long shadows across them. They stared, wondering at his reappearance, his passion, his wild animal howling. Their mother rose from her basket chair and came towards him, worried, annoyed, saying, 'Stop it, stop it, Ravi. Don't be a baby. Have you hurt yourself?' Seeing him attended to, the children went back to clasping their hands and chanting 'The grass is green, the rose is red...'

But Ravi would not let them. He tore himself out of his mother's grasp and pounded across the lawn into their midst, charging at them with his head lowered so that they scattered in surprise. 'I won, →

I won, I won,' he bawled, shaking his head so that the big tears flew.
'Raghu didn't find me. I won, I won –'

It took them a minute to grasp what he was saying, even who he was.
They had quite forgotten him. Raghu had found all the others long
ago. There had been a fight about who was to be It next. It had been
so fierce that their mother had emerged from her bath and made
them change to another game. Then they had played another and
another. Broken mulberries form the tree and eaten them. Helped
the driver wash the car when their father returned from work. Helped
the gardener water the beds till he roared at them and swore he would
complain to their parents. The parents had come out, taken up their
positions on the cane chairs. They had begun to play again, sing and
chant. All this time no one had remembered Ravi. Having disappeared from the scene, he had disappeared from their minds. Clean.

'Don't be a fool,' Raghu said roughly, pushing him aside, and even
Mira said, 'Stop howling, Ravi. If you want to play, you can stand at
the end of the line,' and she put him there very firmly.

from **GAMES AT TWILIGHT** by Anita Desai, India

Soaring against the
lush fields of the
Himalayas are two
sisters who usually
have little time for play,
what with going to
school and tending
their family farm.

Photo: Thomas Kelly/
TCS Publishing Partners

AFTER FORTY DAYS, when the child is fully integrated into the community, the routine of going down to the *fincas* begins.

From when I was very tiny, my mother used to take me down to the *finca*, wrapped in a shawl on her back. She told me that when I was about two, I had to be carried screaming onto the lorry because I didn't want to go. I was so frightened I didn't stop crying until we were about halfway there. I remember the journey by lorry very well. I didn't even know what it was, but I knew I hated it because I hate things that smell horrible. The lorry holds about forty people. But in with the people, go the animals (dogs, cats, chickens) which the people from the *Altiplano* take with them while they are in the *finca*. We have to take our animals. It sometimes took two nights and a day from my village to the coast. During the trip the animals and the small children used to dirty the lorry and you'd get people vomiting and wetting themselves. By the end of the journey, the smell – the filth of people and animals – was unbearable.

The lorry is covered with a tarpaulin so you can't see the country-side you're passing through. Most of the journey is spent sleeping because it's so tedious. The stuffiness inside the lorry with the cover on, and the smell of urine and vomit, make you want to be sick yourself just from being in there. By the time we got to the *finca*, we were totally stupefied; we were like chickens coming out of a pot. We were in such a state, we could hardly walk to the *finca*. I made many trips from the *Altiplano* to the coast, but I never saw the countryside we passed through. We heard other lorries and cars, but we didn't ever see them. We never saw any other villages on the way. I saw the wonderful scenery and places for the first time when we were thrown out of the *finca* and had to pay our own way back on the bus.

I remember that from when I was about eight to when I was about ten, we worked in the coffee crop. And after that, I worked on the cotton plantations further down the coast where it was very, very hot. After my first day picking cotton, I woke up at midnight and lit a candle. I saw the faces of my brothers and sisters covered with mosquitoes. I touched my own face, and I was covered too. They were everywhere; in people's mouths and everywhere. Just looking at these insects and thinking about being bitten set me scratching. That was our world. I felt that it would always be the same, always the same. It hadn't ever changed. ■

from **I... RIGOBERTA MENCHÚ** by Rigoberta Menchú, Guatemala

Women and children return home after a wedding in Quetzal-tenango, Guatemala. The brilliant colours of their clothing identify them as descendants of the great Maya civilization.

Photo: Hansruedi Dörig

SLOWLY HE MOVES
to and fro, to and fro,
then faster and faster
he swishes up and down.

His blue shirt
billows in the breeze
like a tattered kite.

The world whirls by:
east becomes west,
north turns to south;
the four cardinal points
meet in his head.

    Mother!
Where did I come from?
When will I wear long trousers?
Why was my father jailed?

from **POEMS OF BLACK AFRICA** (edited by Wole Soyinka)
by Oswald Mbuyisemi Mtshali, Angola

Swinging in Kuito,
the Angolan city
destroyed by civil war.
The city is infested with
landmines.

Photo: Sean Sutton

EARLY ONE MORNING Mahi and Khoshghadam, her sisters-in-law, Asli and Zolikha, and a few other friends, all with their children, took to the hillsides for herb gathering. They would have to start early so as to return to the village before mid-day when the sun would be at its highest, otherwise the heat would be too much for them. They made this journey a few times each season, in the spring, summer and autumn, except winter when the hills would be covered with snow. Each time they went they would look for different kinds of herbs, at different stages of growth. Zolikha was usually one of the group, as she was somewhat older than the others and they looked to her experience and expertise. She would tell them all about the kinds of herbs and their properties, and they would learn how to treat, dry, store and use them. Some of the herbs had to have the oil extracted from them, and the young women would be shown how to do this by the older women.

That day Mahi collected many different bunches of herbs. The women laughed and joked, they ran and played and had just as much fun as their children who played alongside. Mahi and Khoshghadam chased each other over the hills. At times the women would separate from the group and go off in twos or threes, or at times go on their own for a while, and call to each other over the hills, listening to their echoes. They took food, sweets and drinks with them. They had fun, they shared everything, their work, their problems, their complaints, their joy, in everything they were together and this was their strength.

The women from their village always worked in small groups, they did almost everything in each other's company, whether it was sewing, spinning or weaving, they would work away for hours in their friends' houses. Or they would go, together, with their washing to the riverside or to the spring and spend a whole day there, washing and drying on the stones. Some women had their babies strapped on their backs as they worked. They would have fun, make a day of it. Their laughter and chatter mixing with the running of water over the stones. They did little work on their own. When they had major cleaning to do in the house, such as spring-cleaning or whitewashing, they went to each other for help. They worked in twos and threes, and in this way not only was the work finished much quicker, but they had fun doing it. This was the important part, having fun.

from **MAHI'S STORY** by Gohar Kordi, Iran

The women carpet-weavers of Baluchistan – which is the poorest province in Iran – like Mahi in the story, know how to enjoy themselves despite the harshness of their environment.

Photo:
Nasrolah Kasraian

ON THE VERANDA BESIDE THE PANTRY, Purnasashi is busy feeding the menfolk – Poltoo and Pradip – just back from school, and their fathers, Shukhada and Kulada. Shukhada's two younger boys are there too. There's *murki* and *kheer** today. She doles out handfuls of murki from a big basket into each one's bowl, and tops it with a ladle of kheer.

Chobi's eyes glisten. She hasn't had any lunch that afternoon. In fact, she'd forgotten all about it. Now, at the sight of kheer and murki, she suddenly feels very hungry. Flinging her books and writing slate to a corner by the door, she gets a bowl for herself and flops down beside them. 'Me too, Grandma.'

Chobi, too, holds out her bowl. 'You're giving the others more – give me some more too, Grandma. I'm still hungry.'

'There's no more. Look.' Purnasashi holds out the empty bowl for her to inspect.

All of a sudden, Chobi's head burns with rage, and she screams sharp and shrill, 'You gave everyone two helpings, and me just one, and so little too. When Pholtuda or Monida ask for more, you never say it's gone!'

'Well I never!' Purnasashi is struck dumb for a second, and then she lets off, 'Teach her to read and write, and look what happens next! The girl imagines she's as good as these darling boys of mine! Ridiculous! Will you be earning like the boys? All you'll ever be is a shackle on your father's neck. Yes, those days are coming, and pretty soon, when we won't be able to get food down his throat for worrying over how to get you married off...' Purnasashi leaves her words hanging in the air, bringing some more kheer from the pantry, and pours it into Chobi's bowl.

During her wait, the kheer has dried on her fingers. Just as her grandmother serves that extra bit, the girl goes berserk. 'I don't want it!' she yells, and flings the bowl into the courtyard.

How shocking! Purnasashi has never been so shocked in her life. The boys, too, have stopped eating, and are gaping at Chobi in stunned silence.

'Not a girl, no, she's poison ivy!' screams Purnasashi. 'At work – bone lazy; eats like crazy; fiery speeches come so easy.'

Murki is sweet puffed rice. Kheer, milk and rice cooked together until the milk is thick, is flavoured with cardamom and laced with almonds. It is a favourite dessert in Bengal.

from **NABANKUR** (The Germinating Seed) by Sulekha Sanyal, Bangladesh

Firoza, in front of her home on the outskirts of Dhaka, Bangladesh, skips beside the stones she helps her father to break – at 50 US cents for 50 kilos of stone – for use in road construction. Girls often find it harder than boys to get food from their parents if they do not earn money.

Photo: Shahidul Alam/ Drik Picture Library

DO YOU SEE that hummingbird,
spark that ignites
the first ray of sun
in the morning?

Do you see that branch
that restlessly
opens its arms
to the mouth of the wind?

And do you see
how the bud trembles
when the cruel beak
breaks through its corolla
to pierce its most intimate secret?

Or the magical trace
that the sparrows leave
upon the grass
when they kindle their wings in flight?

Or how the warm bushes
alarmed and shy
shrink before being consumed
in the fierce conflagration of midday?

And have you seen
how water surrenders,
silent and gentle,
in the stubborn battle of the rocks?

Or have you heard how
tree and breeze,
jaguar and dove,
sing their song,
dance their dance,
cry out their loneliness,
and shatter their fears
at the brink of the chasm?

All that is only
a moment's grain of sand
crumbling beside the sea
compared to the lightest touch
of your voice and my voice
or your love and my love.

from **THESE ARE NOT SWEET GIRLS** (Poetry by Latin American Women)
by Fanny Carrión de Fierro, Ecuador

Wearing rubber boots
because it's the rainy
season, high up in
the mountains of
Chimborazo, southern
Ecuador, children dance
for Mother Earth as an
expression of their
ancient Quechua and
Aymara cultures.

Photo: Julio Etchart

TOOK THE NOVICE'S VOWS a year later. There are four basic vows: never to take a life, to abstain from stealing, to abstain from falsehood and to practise celibacy. These vows are broken down into ten precepts and these I understood better. There is such a multitude of living things; it is impossible to avoid taking the life of, say, the insects beneath your feet. Yet this is too regarded as taking a life. So there had to be different degrees of killing. A novice or fully ordained monk breaks his vows only if he kills a human being or takes the life of an animal intentionally. A monk must eschew gold, silver and other fineries. He must avoid intoxicating liquors and abstain from dancing. He must not see spectacular shows. These were all viewed as worldly matters which would distract a young mind from its studies.

For a while I was allowed to roam around the monastery, observing its various activities. Many of the boys were younger than me; it was customary for boys as young as seven to become novices. It was said that a boy could first become a novice as soon as he could chase a raven.

My first years in the monastery were like attending school. I began to learn how to read and write. I had to trace over what my teacher had written on a hard wooden board. This was called 'dry writing'. With a bamboo pen I would follow the strokes and curlicues of my teacher's letters. But I was not allowed to dip the pen in ink. After a week of tracing my teacher's script, I graduated to 'wet writing'. I still had to copy the teacher's letters, but now I was writing them on to a wooden board dusted with a thin layer of soot. This procedure lasted for several months. It was a year before I was allowed to write on paper, though that itself was a rare experience, even for older monks. Making paper was a laborious, expensive process and so the results were never wasted.

Learning to read was another hard struggle. Each monastic order had its own set of Buddhist liturgical texts which all monks were required to recite from memory every morning. Another uncle, called Choden la, taught me pe-cha, or scripture. Each day I'd have to recite a text I'd memorised the day before. If I made a mistake I'd have to hold up my left hand so that my teacher could hit it with a cane. Choden la kept a number of leather whips hanging on a pillar. He used to say, 'If you work hard, the whips will stay where they belong.' More often, though, he used the bamboo cane. He'd say, 'Think of the cane whenever you are memorising.'

A novice's life was hard. But the camaraderie that developed among the young monks and the great care shown by my uncle and teacher Wangpo la made things a bit easier. Soon I was either engrossed in my studies or doing simple chores such as cleaning lamps and fetching water.

The day started early. Monks were up by four in the morning and had to finish all private studies by sunrise. I would recite and memorise texts for two or three hours every morning. I can remember my uncle telling me that that was the best time to learn, because it was then that the mind was at its most receptive. A conch shell was blown at sunrise. This summoned all the monks to the morning assembly. My uncle and a few other older monks did not have to attend, but this was a privilege reserved only for monks who had held senior office.

The assembly began with all the novices lining up at the entrance of the hall. The long brass horn was blown and the elders took their seats. The young novices would then recite a prayer of dedication to Je Tsongkapa, the founder of the Gelgugpa sect to which Gadong monastery belonged. After this we could take our seats. We offered prayers for the long life of the Dalai Lama, prayers that the whole world would be free from famine and plague, and prayers that all people could live in peace. Two cups of tea were served during the assembly. One of the duties of a novice was to serve the tea: he had to carry it hundreds of yards from the kitchen to the hall in a vast brass pot. Sometimes the pot was bigger than the novice.

I never had to do the tea round. A novice might avoid doing certain heavy duties if he came from a wealthy family that had made large donations to the monastery. But I still had to attend to such chores as sweeping, cleaning windows and lighting the hundreds of butter lamps. During the festivals there were thousands of butter lamps to light, and afterwards we had to clean and polish them. And my uncle was always giving me errands to run.

Most of my time was devoted to my studies. There were three ways that a monk could live in a monastery. Those with the intellectual aptitude could devote themselves to studying. Others specialised in ritual, and they would become experts in the different ceremonies and offerings and in the intricate sand mandalas which represented the abodes of various deities. Monks who were not intellectually inclined and who found ceremonies tiresome became officials who →

Novice monks play tag in the gardens of the Likir monastery in Ladakh. People here practice the Tibetan form of Buddhism while living cheek-by-jowl with opposing Indian and Chinese troops across the border.

Photo: Eric Bachmann

looked after the monastery's economic interests. They were the business managers who collected loans and taxes from tenants. Some of them conducted trade on the monastery's behalf.

One day, when I was twelve or thirteen, I went back to the shack for lunch and heard my uncle calling me into his room. My immediate thought was that I had done something wrong. My uncle told me to sit down and offered me tea. He pointed to a pile of tea, tsampa and cloths. He said that these were gifts from my aunt's home. Then he lowered his voice and told me that my aunt had died. I can remember how I shivered and how I thought of all the times she had fussed over me. She was the only person I had truly loved. It was with her that I felt most at ease. But now I had grown up and even had responsibilities of my own, such as the supervision of other novices as they carried our their chores.

I forgot about the world outside the monastery and devoted myself to my studies. I memorised more and more texts. I had a good incentive to work hard, because I had noticed that illiterate or lazy monks ended up with the lowliest duties. I found memorising very hard, though some students accomplished it effortlessly. Whenever a student had memorised a particular text, his teacher would ask the abbot to allow the novice to recite the entire text in front of the assembly. This was pretty terrifying. After the daily liturgy, the young monk would stand in front of the assembly and recite his text. I had to do this several times and I remember the silence in the hall, broken only by the slurping of tea. Monks who managed to recite all the liturgical texts like this were said to have passed their examination. But if a monk dried up in front of the assembly, it was considered a disgrace not only for him but also for his teacher. Luckily, I managed to scrape through.

Since these prayers are recited every day, monks tend to remember them for life. But my experience is different. My long confinement in prison has meant that I can no longer remember many of the prayers we recited in Gadong.

Once a monk had mastered all the basic prayers he could go on to further studies. Either you learned directly from your pe-cha teacher, alone or in groups of three or four, or you could learn from sermons given by a respected scholar. Gadong was just a simple village monastery and it didn't have a high reputation for scholarship. But the abbot established what we called she-dra, or a philosophy class. He invited a learned lama from Lhasa to spend a few weeks at Gadong in order to instruct the monks in philosophy.

Geshe Rigzin was one of the noted teachers at Drepung monastery, near Lhasa. Geshe had even taught our own abbot. I began to attend his classes. Simplicity and asceticism were manifest in his manner and appearance. His voice was very soft, sometimes almost inaudible. He spoke in a clear Lhasa dialect but you could detect traces of a foreign accent. Geshe had been born in Kinaur, in the Indian state of Himachal Pradesh, and had come to study at Drepung when he was sixteen. We called him Gyen. Every day for four months he preached sermons and introduced the more complex aspects of Buddhist philosophy. He said that those of us who really wanted to learn should enrol at one of the three great monasteries in Lhasa. He said Gadong monastery was like a well: there was water there, but not enough to swim in and if we really wanted to swim we'd have to find an ocean.

from **FIRE UNDER THE SNOW** by Palden Gyatso, Tibet

 # lost and found

HOLD TIGHT – OR, quite suddenly, you're all alone and don't know where you are. Time passes and childhood friends take their different routes through the maze of apartheid South Africa recreated by Nadine Gordimer. Letting go doesn't come easy – particularly when your mother has just gone to hospital to have another baby, as in the Kenyan story by Charity Waciuma. Pramoedya Ananta Toer in Indonesia begs forgiveness for adopting callous, Western ways and betraying his inheritance, but Wole Soyinka replaces fake traditions with impudent truths in a Nigerian classroom. Sometimes, too, you only find your love as you are about to lose it – Isabel Allende mourns her mother. Liliana Heker describes what its like being left at home alone in Argentina.

THE FARM CHILDREN PLAY TOGETHER when they are small; but once the white children go away to school they don't play together anymore, even in the holidays. Although most of the black children get some sort of schooling, they drop every year further behind the grades passed by white children; the childish vocabulary, the child's exploration of the adventurous possibilities of dam, koppies, mealie lands and veld – there comes a time when the white children have surpassed these with the vocabulary of boarding-school and the possibilities of inter-school sports matches and the kind of adventures seen at the cinema. This usefully coincides with the age of twelve or thirteen; so that by the time early adolescence is reached, the black children are making, along with the bodily changes common to all, an easy transition to adult forms of address, beginning to call their playmates *missus* and *baasie* – little master.

The trouble was Paulus Eysendyck did not seem to realise that Thebedi was now simply one of the crowd of farm children down at the kraal, recognisable in his sisters' old clothes. The first Christmas holidays after he had gone to boarding-school he brought home for Thebedi a painted box he had made in his wood-work class. He had to give it to her secretly because he had nothing for the other children at the kraal. And she gave him, before he went back to school, a bracelet she had made of thin brass wire and the grey-and-white beans of the castor-oil crop his father cultivated. (When they used to play together, she was the one who had taught Paulus how to make clay oxen for their toy spans.) There was a craze, even in the *platteland* towns like the one where he was at school, for boys to wear elephant-hair and other bracelets beside their watch-straps; his was admired, friends asked him to get similar ones for them. He said the natives made them on his father's farm and he would try.

When he was fifteen, six feet tall, and tramping round at school dances with the girls from the 'sister' school in the same town; when he had learnt how to tease and flirt and fondle quite intimately these girls who were the daughters of prosperous farmers like his father; when he had even met one who, at a wedding he had attended with his parents on a nearby farm, had let him do with her in a locked storeroom what people did when they made love – when he was as far from his childhood as all this, he still brought home from a shop in town a red plastic belt and gilt hoop ear-rings for the black girl, Thebedi. She told her father the missus had given these to her as a reward for some work

she had done – it was true she was sometimes called to help out in the farmhouse. She told the girls in the kraal that she had a sweetheart nobody knew about, far away, away on another farm, and they giggled, and teased, and admired her. There was a boy in the kraal called Njabulo who had said he wished he could have bought her a belt and ear-rings.

When the farmer's son was home for the holidays she wandered far from the kraal and her companions. He went for walks alone. They had not arranged this; it was an urge each followed independently. He knew it was she, from a long way off. She knew that his dog would not bark at her. Down at the dried-up river-bed where five or six years ago the children had caught a leguaan one great day – a creature that combined ideally the size and ferocious aspect of the crocodile with the harmlessness of a lizard – they squatted side by side on the earth bank. He told her traveller's tales: about school, about the punishments at school, particularly, exaggerating both their nature and his indifference to them. He told her about the town of Middleburg, which she had never seen. She had nothing to tell but she prompted with many questions, like any good listener. While he talked he twisted and tugged at the roots of white stinkwood and Cape willow trees that looped out of the eroded earth around them. It had always been a good spot for children's games, down there hidden by the mesh of old, ant-eaten trees held in place by vigorous ones, wild asparagus bushing up between the trunks, and here and there prickly-pear cactus sunken-skinned and bristly, like an old man's face, keeping alive sapless until the next rainy season. She punctured the dry hide of a prickly-pear again and again with a sharp stick while she listened. She laughed a lot at what he told her, sometimes dropping her face on her knees, sharing amusement with the cool shady earth beneath her bare feet. She put on her pair of shoes – white sandals, thickly Blanco-ed against the farm dust – when he was on the farm, but these were taken off and laid aside, at the river-bed.

One summer afternoon when there was water flowing there and it was very hot she waded in as they used to do when they were children, her dress bunched modestly and tucked into the legs of her pants. The schoolgirls he went swimming with at dams or pools on neighbouring farms wore bikinis but the sight of their dazzling bellies and thighs in the sunlight had never made him feel what he felt now, when the girl came up to the bank and sat beside him, the drops of water beading →

Swept along by the festivities, a student dressed as a local gold miner dances with a passer-by during Rag Week at Witwatersrand University in Johannesburg.

Photo: Amadeo Vergani

off her dark legs the only points of light in the earth-smelling, deep shade. They were not afraid of one another, they had known one another always; he did with her what he had done that time in the storeroom at the wedding, and this time it was so lovely, so lovely, he was surprised... and she was surprised by it, too – he could see in her dark face that was part of the shade, with her big dark eyes, shiny as soft water, watching him attentively: as she had when they used to huddle over their teams of mud oxen, as she had when he told her about detention weekends at school.

They went to the river-bed often through those summer holidays. They met just before the light went, as it does quickly, and each returned home with the dark – she to her mother's hut, he to the farmhouse – in time for the evening meal. He did not tell her about school or town any more. She did not ask questions any longer. He told her, each time, when they would meet again. Once or twice it was very early in the morning; the lowing of the cows being driven to graze came to them where they lay, dividing them with unspoken recognition of the sound read in their two pairs of eyes, opening so close to each other.

He was a popular boy at school. He was in the second, then the first soccer team. The head girl of the 'sister' school was said to have a crush on him; he didn't particularly like her, but there was a pretty blonde who put up her long hair into a kind of doughnut with a black ribbon round it, whom he took to see films when the schoolboys and girls had a free Saturday afternoon. He had been driving tractors and other farm vehicles since he was ten years old, and as soon as he was eighteen he got a driver's licence and in the holidays, this last year of his school life, he took neighbours' daughters to dances and to the drive-in cinema that had just opened twenty kilometres from the farm. His sisters were married by then; his parents often left him in charge of the farm over the weekend while they visited the young wives and children.

When Thebedi saw the farmer and his wife drive away on a Saturday afternoon, the boot of their Mercedes filled with fresh-killed poultry and vegetables from the garden that it was part of her father's work to tend, she knew that she must come not to the river-bed but up to the house. The house was an old one, thick-walled, dark against the heat. The kitchen was its lively thoroughfare, with servants, food supplies, begging cats and dogs, pots boiling over, washing being damped for ironing, and the big deep-freeze the missus had ordered from town, bearing a crocheted mat and a vase of plastic irises. But the dining-room with the bulging-legged heavy table was shut up in its rich, old smell of soup and tomato sauce. The sitting-room curtains were drawn and the TV set silent. The door of the parents' bedroom was locked and the empty rooms where the girls had slept had sheets of plastic spread over the beds. It was in one of these that she and the farmer's son stayed together whole nights – almost; she had to get away before the house servants, who knew her, came in at dawn. There was a risk someone would discover her or traces of her presence if he took her to his own bedroom, although she had looked into it many times when she was helping out in the house and knew well, there, the row of silver cups he had won at school.

When she was eighteen and the farmer's son nineteen and working with his father on the farm before entering a veterinary college, the young man Njabulo asked her father for her. Njabulo's parents met with hers and the money he was to pay in place of the cows it is customary to give a prospective bride's parents was settled upon. He had no cows to offer; he was a labourer on the Eysendyck farm, like her father. A bright youngster; old Eysendyck had taught him brick-laying and was using him for odd jobs in construction, around the place. She did not tell the farmer's son that her parents had arranged for her to marry. She did not tell him, either, before he left for his first term at the veterinary college, that she thought she was going to have a baby. Two months after her marriage to Njabulo, she gave birth to a daughter. There was no disgrace in that; among her people it is customary for a young man to make sure, before marriage, that the chosen girl is not barren, and Njabulo had made love to her then. But the infant was very light and did not quickly grow darker as most African babies do. Already at birth there was on its head a quantity of straight, fine floss, like that which carries the seeds of certain weeds in the veld. The unfocused eyes it opened were grey flecked with yellow. Njabulo was the matt, opaque coffee-grounds colour that has always been called black; the colour of Thebedi's legs on which beaded water looked oyster-shell blue, the same colour as Thebedi's face, where the black eyes, with their interested gaze and clear whites, were so dominant.

Njabulo made no complaint. Out of his farm labourer's earnings he bought from the Indian store a cellophane-windowed pack containing a pink plastic bath, six napkins, a card of safety pins, a knitted jacket, cap and booties, a dress, and a tin of Johnson's Baby Powder, for Thebedi's baby.

When it was two weeks old Paulus Eysendyck arrived home from the veterinary college for the holidays. He drank a glass of fresh, still-warm milk in the childhood familiarity of his mother's kitchen and heard her discussing with the old house-servant where they could get a reliable substitute to help out now that the girl Thebedi had had a baby. For the first time since he was a small boy he came right into the kraal. It was eleven o'clock in the morning. The men were at work in the lands. He looked about him, urgently; the women turned away, each not wanting to be the one approached to point out where Thebedi lived. Thebedi appeared, coming slowly from the hut Njabulo had built in white man's style, with a tin chimney, and a proper window with glass panes set in straight as walls made of unfired bricks would allow. She greeted him with hands brought together and a token movement representing the respectful bob with which she was accustomed to acknowledge she was in the presence of his father or mother. He lowered his head under the doorway of her home and went in. He said, 'I want to see. Show me.'

She had taken the bundle off her back before she came out into the light to face him. She moved between the iron bedstead made up with Njabulo's checked blankets and the small wooden table where the pink plastic bath stood among food and kitchen pots, and picked up the bundle from the snugly-blanketed grocer's box where it lay. The infant was asleep; she revealed the closed, pale, plump tiny face, with a bubble of spit at the corner of the mouth, the spidery pink hands stirring. She took off the woollen cap and the straight fine hair flew up after it in static electricity, showing gilded strands here and there. He said nothing. She was watching him as she had done when they were little, and the gang of children had trodden down a crop in their games or transgressed in some other way for which he, as the farmer's son, the white one among them, must intercede with the farmer. She disturbed the sleeping face by scratching or tickling gently at a cheek with one finger, and slowly the eyes opened, saw nothing, were still asleep, and then, awake, no longer narrowed, looked out at them, grey with yellowish flecks, his own hazel eyes.

He struggled for a moment with the grimace of tears, anger and self-pity. She could not put out her hand to him. He said, 'You haven't been near the house with it?'

She shook her head.

'Never?'

Again, she shook her head.

'Don't take it out. Stay inside. Can't you take it away somewhere? You must give it to someone –'

She moved to the door with him.

He said, 'I'll see what I will do. I don't know.' And then he said: 'I feel like killing myself.'

Her eyes began to glow, to thicken with tears. For a moment there was the feeling between then that used to come when they were alone down at the river-bed.

He walked out.

Two days later, when his mother and father had left the farm for the day, he appeared again. The women were away on the lands, weeding, as they were employed to do as casual labour in summer; only the very old remained, propped up on the ground outside the huts in the flies and the sun. Thebedi did not ask him in. The child had not been well; it had diarrhoea. He asked where its food was. She said, 'The milk comes from me.' He went into Njabulo's house, where the child lay; she did not follow but stayed outside the door and watched without seeing an old crone who had lost her mind, talking to herself, talking to the fowls who ignored her.

She thought she heard small grunts from the hut, the kind of infant grunt that indicates a full stomach, a deep sleep. After a long time, long or short she did not know, he came out and walked away with plodding stride (his father's gait) out of sight, towards his father's house.

The baby was not fed during the night and although she kept telling Njabulo it was sleeping, he saw for himself in the morning that it was dead. He comforted her with words and caresses. She did not cry but simply sat, staring at the door. Her hands were cold as dead chickens' feet to his touch.

Njabulo buried the little baby where the farm workers were buried, in the place in the veld the farmer had given them. Some of the mounds had been left to weather away unmarked, other were covered with stones and a few had fallen wooden crosses. He was going to make a cross but before it was finished the police came and dug up the grave and took away the dead baby: someone – one of the labourers? their women? – had reported that the baby was almost white, that, strong and healthy, it had died suddenly after a visit by the farmer's son. →

Pathological tests on the infant corpse showed intestinal damage not always consistent with death by natural causes.

Thebedi went for the first time to the country town where Paulus had been to school, to give evidence at the preparatory examination into the charge of murder brought against him. She cried hysterically in the witness box, saying yes, yes (the gilt hoop ear-rings swung in her ears), she saw the accused pouring liquid into the baby's mouth. She said he had threatened to shoot her if she told anyone.

More than a year went by before, in that same town, the case was brought to trial. She came to court with a new-born baby on her back. She wore gilt hoop ear-rings; she was calm, she said she had not seen what the white man did in the house.

Paulus Eysendyck said he had visited the hut but had not poisoned the child.

The defence did not contest that there had been a love relationship between the accused and the girl, or that intercourse had taken place, but submitted there was no proof that the child was the accused's.

The judge told the accused there was strong suspicion against him but not enough proof that he had committed the crime. The court could not accept the girl's evidence because it was clear she had committed perjury either at this trial or at the preparatory examination. There was the suggestion in the mind of the court that she might be an accomplice in the crime; but again, insufficient proof.

The judge commended the honourable behaviour of the husband (sitting in court in a brown-and-yellow quartered golf cap bought for Sundays) who had not rejected his wife and had 'even provided clothes for the unfortunate infant out of his slender means'.

The verdict on the accused was 'not guilty'.

The young white man refused to accept the congratulations of press and public and left the court with his mother's raincoat shielding his face from photographers. His father said to the press, 'I will try and carry on as best I can to hold up my head in the district.'

Interviewed by the Sunday papers, who spelled her name in a variety of ways, the black girl, speaking in her own language, was quoted beneath her photograph: 'It was a thing of our childhood, we don't see each other any more.'

from **CRIMES OF CONSCIENCE** by Nadine Gordimer, South Africa

Dancing in Soweto, Johannesburg. The children's future hangs in the balance as South Africa charts a new course away from apartheid.

Photo: Amedeo Vergani

ONE YEAR, as the last heavy rains were falling, my mother went to the Local Council Hospital. Before she left she called us children together and said, 'You will have to look after yourselves for a few days because Mummy is going to have a baby and Papa will be busy working.'

We asked how long she was to be away and she said for one week. This seemed an eternity to me, at the age of nine or ten, because I depended on her so much. Although my grandmother came and spoiled me, I still longed for my mother to be back. I hated to think of the baby she would bring back from the hospital which would, I thought, take my place in her affections, though I was not even then the youngest.

As I stood waving to my parents in the bus on their way to the hospital, the rain became lighter and lighter as it fell in bright, slanting showers. Sometimes the sun shone through the rain and a warmer breeze blew. A rainbow formed in the sky and in my excitement I forgot about my parents' departure. I ran to my grandmother who was cooking in our grass-thatched kitchen and breathlessly asked her, 'What is a rainbow?'

'It is a long, bright snake that dwells in the water. When the rain

I FELT LIKE AN ORPHAN of the modern age, without even traditional ties to kith and kin. I had left East Java to become a person. And now the love and compassion of my mother stood before me as a judge who would allow no appeal.

'Why don't you say anything, Child? You can't speak with your heart anymore. You've become a black Dutchman in Javanese clothes. If that's what you want, then so be it. But tell your mother what she should do in order to love you.'

'Ah, Mother, love has no conditions. Mother will always love me, as you have done in the past, do now, and will do in the future. So bless me in my struggle to achieve my ideals.'

'Keep talking. You have begun to talk. You used to have so much to talk about, you knew so many stories that you became a man of letters. Now you look so tired. Speak, Child. Tell me all, so that once again I can feel I am a mother worthy of her child. Don't think about whether I will like what you say or not. I know your world is far away from your mother's. But perhaps I might understand a little of what you say.'

'I once told Mother about the French Revolution.'

'I remember. If everyone had equal rights like that, then what rights would a mother have over her children?'

'She would have the right to love them, Mother, to raise them and educate them.'

'Is that all?'

Her love was now playing the part of prosecutor and judge! How must I answer?

'I'm so sorry for you, Child; you're so tortured by my question. Listen, I demand nothing of you. As long as I can see you I am happy, and if I can touch you, then I am even happier. But to see you knotted up inside like this makes me suffer too. Become whatever you like. Become a Dutchman. I will not object.'

'Forgiveness, Mother, please do not say that again.' I uttered my request in a pathetically pleading voice. 'You sent me to school so that, as a Javanese, I would have the wisdom and knowledge of Europe. Both of those things change people, Mother.'

'I understand, Child, but should they not change people for the better, and not for the worse.'

'Your blessing, Mother, your blessing.'

'But you must not suffer so much.'

'I do not suffer.'

'Don't you think I know my own child? I have known you since you were in my womb. I have known your voice since your first cry. Even without your letters, without seeing your face, from far away, a mother's heart can always tell, Child. How much you have suffered so that you can become what you want. You do not even want to share any of it with your mother. Yes, I know that Europeans want to bear all their burdens themselves. But is that necessary when you have a mother?'

'Tell me, Mother,' I begged.

'You have caught the European's disease, Child. You want everything for yourself just as you tell about them in your stories.'

'Mother!'

'That is Europe's disease. Shouldn't you learn to think of others too? Haven't I told you, learn to be thankful? Don't say anything, wait. You once told me yourself that, for Europeans, when they say "thank you" it is just a pretence. They do not say it with their hearts. You have become like that, Child. I haven't forgotten your stories. The clever try to become cleverer, the rich, richer. No one has any gratitude in their hearts. Everyone is hurrying around trying to be better. Isn't that what you yourself have told me? They all suffer. Their desires and ideals become monsters that rule over them. Do you remember?'

'I remember, Mother.'

'So what is the use of the French Revolution then?' and her voice was so gentle, as it had been ever since the first time I heard it. 'You said it was to free men from the burdens made by other men. Wasn't that it? That is not Javanese. A Javanese does something with no other motive than to do it. Orders come from Allah, from the gods, from the Raja. After a Javanese has carried out the order, he will feel satisfied because he has become himself. And then he waits for the next order. So the Javanese are grateful, they give thanks. They are not preyed upon by monsters within themselves.'

'Mother, I have learned much in my studies. I know now that life is not so simple.'

'What teacher has told you that, my child? In bygone days, your ancestors always taught you that there was nothing so simple as life. You are born, you eat and drink, you grow, bring children into the world, and do good.'

from **FOOTSTEPS** by Pramoedya Ananta Toer, Indonesia

Teenage boys in the south of Nias Island, Indonesia must leap over obstacles without touching a 'jump-stone' in order to become men. This custom developed from the training of warriors who needed to vault over the walls of fortified villages of rival Nias clans.

Photo:
Michael Macintyre /
The Hutchison Library

HE DROPPED THE NEEDLE ARM GENTLY. 'The singer is Paul Robeson, Maren. You may console yourself with the thought that he, like the rest of us, would most certainly have undergone the normal experience of hearing his voice break. Now listen to the poem...'

And did those feet in ancient time
Walk upon England's mountains green
And was the holy Lamb of God
On England's pleasant pastures seen...?

Paul Robeson's booming voice filled the room, overwhelming the young listeners. But it was not until the second verse began that Maren felt profoundly stirred, feeling an intensity of faith that he could not precisely define, only that it was different from the narrow religious kind, that it embraced the entire human universe, yet contained a personal message for every being. In his mind, it bore an affinity to the words of the illuminated manuscript, *'Four score and twenty years ago...',* reinforcing the sensation of a profound universal discovery. The clouds had opened and a rain of combative peroration was streaming down, very different from the sermons and the hymning of St Peter's, Akè, yet close in spirit to the *oguso** torchlight procession of Ransome-Kuti's 'Grammarians' on Foundation Day, all the way from Igbehin Downs to Akè hills, belting out the march, *'He who would valiant be',* and closing the week-long celebrations with the Egba anthem *L'Ori Oke ati Petele...* Paul Robeson and William Blake – he could imagine them both in step with the white-uniformed boys, their valiant steps in consonance from the downs of Igbehin, against the backdrop if Olumo rocks, winding past the cenotaph of the great warrior Lisabi, and filing into St Peter's Church, transformed at this time of the year into a huge, festal theatre...

Bring me my Bow of burning gold!
Bring me my Arrows of desire!
Bring me my Spear! O clouds, unfold!
Bring me my Chariot of fire.
I will not cease from Mental Fight,
Nor shall my Sword sleep in my hand...

Back from leave, English master Kaye held the piece of paper at arm's length, his face a map of anguish; even his ragged moustache appeared to have drooped in despair as he shook his head slowly from side to side, groaning, 'What have I done, Maren, what have I done?' The boy watched him, wondering what could have driven him to despair in the lines he had crafted with such care.

'Read it aloud, Maren,' and he held it out to him on the extreme tip of his fingers, as if he was afraid of catching a terrible disease from the sheet. 'It is good training to read one's poetic effusions aloud. One learns a lot, Maren; one learns a lot by listening carefully to oneself, be it poetry or prose, just as in answering questions in class. Read it aloud, Master Maren.'

The boy took back the offering he had penned in tribute to William Blake, feeling relieved that he was being made to read it in the staff-room, not in front of the entire class, with Kaye's caustic comments cutting him to the quick.

Is Africa a land so base
Are we born into servitude
Have we to bear that yoke always
Of slavery in such magnitude?
Perhaps our acts are not so smart
To those who come our land to spoil
Have they not taken the better part
Of our ancestral, arable soil.

He paused. For a long moment, teacher and pupil stared at each other. 'The next verse, Maren, the next verse.'

The boy shook his head. 'No, sir, I don't think I want to read it.'

Kaye sighed. 'I should think not, Maren. The effort, of course, is to be applauded, but this is not quite the kind of flattery of which imitation sometimes is held to be. Mr William Blake,' and his voice turned dolorous, 'Mr William Blake must be turning in his grave.'

* *fibre kindling.*

from **IBADAN** by Wole Soyinka, Nigeria

THERE IS NO DEATH, daughter. People die only when we forget them,' my mother explained shortly before she left me. 'If you remember me, I will be with you always.'

'I will remember you,' I promised.

'Now go call your godmother.'

I went to look for the cook, the enormous mulatto woman who had helped me into the world and who at the proper time had carried me to be christened.

'Take good care of my girl, *madrina*. I'm leaving her in your hands,' my mother said, discreetly wiping away the thread of blood trickling down her chin. Then she took my hand and, with her eyes, kept telling me how much she loved me, until a fog clouded her gaze and life faded from her body without a sound. For a few seconds I thought I saw something translucent floating in the motionless air of the room, flooding it with blue radiance and perfuming it with a breath of musk, but then everything was normal again, the air merely air, the light yellow, the smell the simple smell of every day. I took my mother's face in my hands and moved it back and forth, calling 'Mama, Mama,' stricken by the silence that had settled between us.

'Everyone dies, it's not so important,' my *madrina* said, cutting off my mother's long hair with three clicks of the scissors, planning to sell it later in a wig shop. 'We need to get her out of here before the *patrón* discovers her and makes me bring her to the laboratory.'

I picked up the braid of hair, wrapped it around my neck, and huddled in a corner with my head between my knees; I did not cry, because I still did not realise the magnitude of my loss. I stayed there for hours, perhaps all night, until two men came in, wrapped the body in the bed's only cover, and carried it away without a word. Then the room was pervaded by unremitting emptiness.

After the modest funeral coach had left, my *madrina* came to look for me. She had to strike a match to see me because the room was in shadows; the light bulb had burned out and dawn seemed to have stopped at the threshold. She found me in a little bundle on the floor. She called me twice by name, to bring me back to reality: Eva Luna... Eva Luna. In the flickering flame of the match, I saw large feet in house slippers and the hem of a cotton dress. I looked up and met her moist eyes. She smiled and at that instant the uncertain spark died out; then I felt her bend over in the darkness. She picked me up in her stout arms, settled me on her lap, and began to rock me, humming some soft African lament to put me to sleep.

from **EVA LUNA** by Isabel Allende, Chile

Plaiting *icchu* grass into cords for use in making bridges in Peru; a daughter watches her mother in order to memorize the skill for future use.

Photo: Hansruedi Dörig

HOW MUCH LONGER till Mom comes home?'

It's the fourth time Mariana has asked that same question. The first time her sister Lucia answered that she'd be back real soon; the second time, that how the heck was she to know when Mom would be back; the third time she didn't answer – she just raised her eyebrows and stared at Mariana. Following which, Mariana decided that things weren't going all that well and that the best thing to do was not to ask any more questions. *Anyhow,* she thought, *why do I want Mom to come back, if I'm here with Lucia...* she corrected herself: *Why do I want Mom to come back, if I'm here with my big sister.* She blinked, deeply moved by the thought. Big sisters look after little sisters, she said to herself, as if reciting a poem; *how lucky to have a big sister.* Lucia, with large guardian angel wings, hovered for a second over Mariana's head. But in a flash the winged image was replaced by another, one which returned every time their mother left them on their own: Lucia, eyes bulging out of their sockets, hair in a furious tangle, was pointing at her with a gun. Sometimes there was no gun: Lucia would pounce on her, trying to rip Mariana's eyes out with her nails. Or strangle her. The reason was always the same: Lucia had gone mad.

It is a well known fact that mad people kill normal people, which meant that if Lucia went mad when they were alone together, she'd kill her, Mariana: that was obvious. Therefore Mariana decides to abandon her good intentions and asks again, for the fourth time: 'How much longer till Mom comes home?'

Lucia stops reading and sighs.

'What I'd like to know,' she says, and Mariana thinks: she said *'I'd like to know'; does one say 'I would like to know' or 'I should like to know'?* – 'What I'd like to know is why in God's name you always need Mom around.'

'No.' *Now she'll ask me 'No what?' She always manages to interfere,* but Lucia says nothing, and Mariana continues, 'I was just curious, that's all.'

'At twelve.'

'What do you mean, at twelve!' Mariana cries out. 'But it's only ten to nine now!'

'I mean at twelve, six and six,' Lucia says.

Mariana howls with laughter at the joke; she laughs so hard that for a moment she thinks she'll die laughing. To tell the truth, she can't imagine there being anyone on earth as funny as her sister. *She's the*

funniest, nicest person in the world, and she'll never go mad. Why should she go mad, she, who's absolutely terrific?

'Lu,' she says adoringly, 'let's play something, Okay? Let's, Okay?'

'I'm reading.'

'Reading what?'

'Mediocre Man.'

'Ah.' *I bet now she'll ask me if I know what mediocre man means, and I won't know, and she'll say then, 'Why do you say "Ah," you idiot?'* Quickly she asks, 'Lu, I can't remember, what does mediocre man mean?'

'The mediocre man is the man who has no ideals in life.'

'Ah.' This puts her mind at rest, because she certainly has ideals in life. She always imagines herself already grown up, when all her problems will be over, and everyone understands her, and things turn out fine, and the world is wonderful. That's having ideals in life.

'Lu,' she says, 'we, I mean, you and I, we're not mediocre, are we?'

'A pest,' Lucia says, 'that's what you are.'

'Lucia, why is it that you are so unpleasant to everyone, huh?'

'Listen, Mariana. Do you mind just letting me read in peace?'

'You're unpleasant to everyone. That's terrible, Lucia. You fight with Mom, you fight with Dad. With everyone.' Mariana lets out a deep sigh. 'You give your parents nothing but trouble, Lucia.'

'Mariana, I wish you'd just drop dead, okay?'

'You're horrible, Lucia, horrible! You don't tell anyone to drop dead, not your worst enemy, and certainly not your own sister.'

'That's it, now start crying, so that afterwards they scream at me and say that I torture you.'

'Afterwards? When afterwards? Do you know exactly when Mom will be back?'

'Just afterwards.' Lucia has gone back to reading *Mediocre Man.*

'Afterwards is afterwards,' lifting her eyes and frowning as if she were meditating on something very important. 'The future, I mean.'

'What future? You said Mom would be back very soon.'

'No. Yes, of course, no. Is she coming back very soon or isn't she coming back very soon?'

Lucia glares at Mariana; then she seems to remember something and smiles briefly.

'And anyway, what does it matter?' she says and shrugs her shoulders.

'What do you mean, what does it matter? you don't know what you're saying, do you? If someone comes home very soon, it means she →

The colourful 'artists' district' of Buenos Aires may be a good place to grow up in, but it still can't quell childish anxieties.

Photo: Steve Morgan/ Evironmental Images

comes home very soon, doesn't it?'

'If someone comes home, yes.'

'What?'

'I just said that if someone comes home, then yes. Will you please let me read?'

'You're a cow, that's what you are! What you really want is for Mom never to come home again!'

'It has nothing to do with my wanting it or not,' she explains. 'What I'm saying is that it simply doesn't matter if Mom is here or there.'

'What do you mean, there?'

'Just there; anywhere; it's all the same.'

'Why the same?'

Lucia rests her chin on both her hands and stares gravely at Mariana.

'Listen, Mariana,' she says, 'I've got something to tell you. Mom doesn't exist.'

Mariana jumps.'Don't be stupid, okay?' she says, trying to look calm. 'You know Mom doesn't like you saying stupid things like that.'

'They're not stupid things. Anyway, who cares what Mom says, if Mom doesn't exist?'

'Lu, I'm telling you for the last time: I-don't-like-you-say-ing-stu-pid-things, okay?'

'Look, Mariana,' Lucia says in a tired tone of voice. 'I'm not making it up; there's a whole theory about it, a book.'

'What does it say, the book?'

'What I just said. That nothing really exists. That we imagine the world.'

'What do we imagine about the world?'

'Everything.'

from **BERKLEY OR MARIANA OF THE UNIVERSE** by Liliana Heker, Argentina

# **endpiece**

 **ON BEING THE CHILD** in the picture, by Shashi Tharoor.

MAKE THIS CHILD SMILE AGAIN,' the black type on the crumpled, glossy news weekly page read. 'All it takes is five dollars a month.'

Joseph stared at the picture sandwiched between the two halves of the caption. He had seen it a thousand times – the tattered clothes, the dark, intense, pleading eyes, the grubby little fingers thrust tightly into a sullenly closed mouth. The photo that had launched the most successful, worldwide appeal in HELP's history, four years ago. His picture.

As usual, he viewed it once more with that curious detachment that had come to him during those last four years. He could not see it as a photograph of himself, a record of his past, a souvenir of his younger childhood. It was not personal enough for that; it was in the public domain, part of an advertisement, a poster, a campaign, and now an ageing magazine clipping in his hand. The little boy who stared out at him was not him, Joseph Kumaran; he was part of a message, defined by a slogan, serving a purpose, and the fact that he was Joseph Kumaran did not matter. It never had.

Joseph looked once more at the picture, as if he had five times already during the flight, as if to reassure himself that he knew what he was doing on this large, cold, humming monster hurtling him towards a strange land he had known only in postage stamps. That's what this is all about, he wanted the picture to say. That's who you are and the reason why you are on an unfamiliar thing called an aeroplane and why your feet don't touch the ground but your toes feel cold and you have to put a belt around your waist that stops you from leaning forward comfortably to eat the strange food they expect you to get at with plastic forks and knives, sealed impossibly in polythene, while you wish you could pluck up the nerve to ask the poised, distant and impossibly tall, white lady to help you, help you with a blanket and two pillows and some real food you can eat without trying to gnaw at sealed packages of cutlery...

He folded the picture again and pushed it into the pocket of the tight little blazer he had been given the day he left the HELP office with Sister Celine to go to the airport. It had been sent with a bundle of old clothes for the disaster relief collection, he had learned, and though it was a little small for him it was just the thing to smarten him up for the trip to the United States. 'Always be smart, Joseph,' Sister Celine had said. 'Let them know you're poor but you're smart, because we knew how to bring you up.' Joseph sat back, his feet dangling from the aeroplane seat, and looked at the largely uneaten food on the tray. When he thought of food he could remember the day of the photograph. He had been seven then: that was the day he had learned he was seven.

'How old's that little kid? The one with the torn white shirt?'

'He's about seven. No one's really sure. He came here when he was a little child, We couldn't really tell when he'd been born.'

'About seven, eh? Looks younger,' click, whirr. 'Might be what I'm looking for. Get him away from that food, Sister, will you please? We want a hungry child, not a feeding one.'

Suddenly, a large white hand interposed among the tiny outstretched brown ones crowded at the table, pulling Joseph's away. 'Come here, Joseph. This nice man wants to see you.'

'But I want to eat, Sister.' Desperation, pleading in his voice. He knew what could happen if he was too late. There would be no food left for him: it had happened before. And today was his favourite day, with crisp papadams in the kanji gruel. He had watched the cooks rip up and fry the papadams from behind the kitchen door, and he'd tried to get to the table early so he wouldn't miss out on his share. He'd had to fight the bigger boys to stay there, too. But what determined resistance had preserved, Sister Celine was taking away.

'Please, Sister, please.'

'Later, child. Now behave yourself.' He was dragging his feet and she was pulling him quite firmly by the left hand. 'And if you don't walk properly I shall have to take the cane to you.' He straightened up quickly; he knew the cane well and did not want it again.

Would the air-hostess take a cane to him if he asked her for a fork and knife? Of course she wouldn't, he knew that. He knew his nervousness was silly, unnecessary. He was suddenly hungry, but he didn't know how to attract her attention. She was giving a man a drink several rows in front of Joseph.

'Miss!' he called softly. His voice came out huskily, tripping over dry obstacles in his throat, She didn't hear him; he wished desperately that she would catch his eye, and he trained his look on her with such fearful intensity it was unbelievable she should not notice. 'Miss!' he called again, waving his hand. She was sticking a pin into the head-rest of the man who'd bought the drink, and she still didn't hear.

Learning to write in the cold, clear air of Lhasa, Tibet, where children must study in the Mandarin Chinese of the occupying forces.

Photo: Janet Wishnetsky

'Miss!' This time it was too loud. It seemed to Joseph that everyone in the plane had turned to look at him, as if he had done something very odd. There were a couple of smiles, but for the most part people looked disapproving, frowning their displeasure at him and making comments to their neighbours. Joseph's dark cheeks flushed red with embarrassment.

The air-hostess straightened up, controlled her irritation, and smiled sweetly but briskly as she walked down to him.

'Can-I-have-a-knife-and-fork-please?' The words came out in a rush, Sister Angela's diction lessons forgotten in his anxiety.

She hardly seemed to pause in her stride. 'It's on your tray – here, on the side, see? In this packet.' And she lifted the packet, placed it on top of the napkin for him to see, and before he could say anything more, strode off down the aisle.

'Hold it there, kid.' Joseph, seven, wanting *papadams*, confronted American slang for the first time in the person of a large, white man with a moustache and a camera. To little Joseph, everything seemed large about the man: his body, his moustache, his camera. A large hand pushed him back a little and a voice boomed: 'Seems rather small for his age.'

'Infant malnutrition. Mother died in childbirth and his father brought him through the forest alone. These tribals are astonishingly hardy. God knows how he survived without any permanent damage.'

'So there's nothing really wrong with him, right? I mean, his brain's okay and everything? I've gotta be sure I'm selling the American public poverty and not retardation, if you see what I mean. So he's normal, huh?'

'Just a little stunted.' Sister Celine, quiet, precise. *Click, whirr.* Lights exploded at him. His eyes widened.

'Let's take him outside, if you don't mind. I'd like to use the sun – I'm not too sure of my flash.'

'Yes, of course, Mr Cleaver. Come, Joseph.'

He squirmed out of the nun's grasp. 'But, Sister, I want to eat.'

'Later. Now if you're difficult there'll be no lunch at all for you.'

Resentfully, he followed them out into the courtyard. He stood there sullenly, staring his quiet hatred at the large man. *Click, whirr, click.*

'Move him to the side a bit, won't you, Sister?'

It was being pushed around that made him thrust his fingers into his mouth, as much in self-protection as in appeasement of his palate.

The photographer clicked again.

Joseph turned to look at the air-hostess' retreating back in profound dismay. Why hadn't he told her that he knew he had a knife and fork, but he didn't know how to get at them? Why hadn't he made clear what exactly was the help he needed? Why had he been so scared?

He drew himself even more deeply into his seat and looked around nervously. His neighbour, staring out of the window, smiled briefly, mechanically at him. Joseph could not ask him to help. Or could he? The man turned from the window to a magazine he was reading over dinner. Joseph's resolution faded.

That day, after the photographs, there had been no *papadams* left for him. Only cold *kanji*; the *papadams* were already finished.

'See – I told you you could have lunch later,' the nun said. 'Here's your lunch now.'

But I wanted the papadams, he wanted to scream in rage and frustration. And why did you need to take me away from my papadams? What was so important about that man with the camera that you had to deprive me of something I've been waiting a month to enjoy? But he did not say all that. He could not. Instead, the lump in his throat almost choking him, he flung the tin plate of gruel to the ground and burst into tears.

'Good heavens – what's the matter with him today? Very well, no lunch for you then, Joseph. And you will clean this mess off the floor and come to my office as soon as you have done so, so that you may be suitably punished for your ingratitude. There are many little boys not as fortunate as you are, Joseph Kumaran. And don't you forget it.' Sniffing back his misery, Joseph knew he would not forget it. He would have six strokes of the cane to remember it by.

How could he ask his neighbour to help open the packet? He was engrossed in his magazine. And he was eating. It seemed so wrong, and so embarrassing. Joseph tried to speak, but the words would not come out.

At the end of the aisle, another stewardess was already bringing tea or coffee around. The other passengers seemed to be finishing their meals. They would take his tray away from him and he would not even had eaten. A panic, irrational but intense, rose to flood him.

He struggled with the packet. He tried to tear it, gnaw at it, rip it open. It would not give way. The cutlery inside the packet jangled; at one point he hit a cup on his tray and nearly broke it. Joseph's attempts became even wilder and he made little noises of desperation.

'Here,' his neighbour's strong voice said. 'Let me help you.'

Joseph turned to him in gratitude. He had hoped his desperation would be apparent and attract assistance. It had worked.

'Thank you,' he managed to say. 'I didn't know how to open it.'

'It's quite easy,' his neighbour said.

The first copies of the photographs arrived at the HELP Centre a few weeks after the photographer had gone. Joseph had almost forgotten the incident, even the caning, though the frustration of the *papadam*-less gruel remained. One of the nuns called him to Sister Eva's office excitedly.

'Look, Joseph – these are the pictures the nice man took, the day you were so bad,' Sister Celine told him. 'This is you.'

Joseph looked at the black-and-white image without curiosity. He would rather not have seen it, rather not have been reminded of their perverse cruelty to him that day. He stared at the picture, made no comment and looked away.

'It's going to be used in a worldwide appeal.' Sister said. 'Your picture will be in every important magazine in the world. Doesn't that make you happy, Joseph?'

He had learned to be dutiful. 'Yes, Sister.' he said.

The man in the seat next to him turned the polythene packet around, slipped out a flap and deftly extracted a fork and a knife. He handed them to Joseph with a cordial smile.

'There – you see, easy.'

'Thank you.' Joseph, taking the implements from the man, felt his ears burning with shame. So there had been no need to try and tear open the packet after all. There was a flap. He turned single-mindedly to the food, wanting to shut the rest of the world, witness to his humiliation, out of his sight and hearing.

The first MAKE THIS CHILD SMILE AGAIN poster was put up in the HELP office just behind Sister Eva's desk, so those who came in would be struck by it as soon as they entered and looked for her. It was put up without any fuss or ceremony, and Joseph only knew it was there because the door to Sister Eva's office had been open when he and a group of boys had been walking down the corridor to their daily classes. It was one of the other boys who had noticed it first and drawn everyone else's attention to it.

The slogan soon became a joke. 'Smile, Joseph, smile,' his friends would tease him. And if he was in a particularly angry mood, one of the boys would ask him with mock gravity, 'Has anyone got five dollars?' Sometimes Joseph would only get angrier, but sometimes he would be provoked to smile at them. They used to call it 'the five-dollar smile.' The food was terrible. It was totally unfamiliar to Joseph's taste buds, anyway, and he did not enjoy it. There was, however, a bowl of fruit salad on the tray that contained little diced apples. He ate those, spilling some on the seat and the floor. He did not know whether to be happy about the pieces he had eaten or sad about the ones he had lost. He looked around to see if anyone was watching him. No one was. He tried to pick up a little piece of apple from the floor but the tray was in his way and he couldn't reach down far enough. It was frustrating. On balance, he felt miserable.

The air-hostess swished by to collect his tray. Would he like some tea? Joseph said, 'Yes.' Actually he wanted coffee but he was scared that if he said 'no' to the tea he might not be offered any coffee either. Why couldn't they have offered him coffee first? he thought, as the pale, brown liquid filled his cup. It was so unfair.

He was, not surprisingly, the first child to be 'adopted'. Other people who responded to the campaign had sent in their five dollars for the first month, and their pledges for a year or two years or a decade or a lifetime, for any child HELP wanted to rescue. But three couples insisted their money go to one specific child – the child in the photograph. They had seen his sad, little face and they wanted to make him smile again. No one else. Their five dollars was for Joseph Kumaran's tiny little fingers to come out of his hungry little mouth. And they insisted on being allowed to adopt him alone.

The nuns had sighed when those letter came in. 'Oh, what a nuisance some people are,' Sister Eva said. 'I have half a mind to return their money to them. It's none of their business to tell us where their money should go.' But Sister Eva had kept the money and the pledges anyway – from all three couples. Joseph Kumaran's five-dollar smile was actually netting HELP fifteen dollars a month.

So every month Joseph would have to sit down and, in his neat, strained little hand, write a letter to each of his fosterparents, thousands of miles away, telling them how good and grateful he was. 'Today we had catechism and I learned the story of how Lot's wife turned into a banana tree,' he would write to one couple. (Salt was an expensive commodity in those parts and the nuns didn't want →

the children to derive the wrong lessons from the Bible.) Then he would copy the same line out neatly onto the other two letters. As he grew older, Sister Celine would no longer dictate the letters but let him write them himself and correct them before they were mailed. 'Sister Angela has told me about America,' he wrote once. 'Is it true that everyone is rich there and always has plenty to eat?' Sister Celine did not like that, scored it out and was later seen speaking sternly to Sister Angela.

The steward was coming down the aisle selling earphones. Joseph had seen him doing that as the flight began, and though he did not know what earphones were, he had discovered that they cost money and that people put them into their ears. He shook his head vigorously when asked whether he wanted one. But his anxious eyes rolled in curiosity as his neighbour, who had also declined the first time, looked at the movie handbill in approbation, produced green notes and silver coins and was rewarded with a polythene packet. From this emerged a contraption even stranger at close quarters than it had seemed from a distance.

The curtains were drawn across the aeroplane windows; a screen was lowered at the head of the cabin; images flickered on the whiteness ahead. Joseph stared, transfixed, rapt. His neighbour had plugged in his earphone and was obviously listening to something Joseph could not hear. Titles began to appear on the screen.

Joseph desperately wanted to hear the movie, too.

He would get the letters in reply from his fosterparents. Initially, they were as frequent as his monthly letters to them, but later their interest seemed to flag and he would get only occasional replies. One couple seemed the nicest – they would always apologise profusely whenever their letters were too late and they would always ask about him, his schoolwork, his games. On Christmas they would send little gifts that Sister Celine would let him open but which he would have to share with the other children. Joseph liked their coloured notepaper, the lady's handwriting, which was so easy to read, and the lingering smell of perfume that still clung to each sheet of stationery. Frequently he would hold it up to his face, smothering his nose in it, smelling America.

One day, after several letters to this couple, he became bolder. 'It is very hot here at this time of year,' he had written in the version approved by Sister Celine. 'I suppose it is cooler in America.' But while copying the corrected draft out neatly onto an aerogramme, he added: 'I think I would enjoy America very much.' He told no one about the addition, sealed the aerogramme and waited excitedly for a reply.

When it came, there was no reference to what he had written. But Joseph did not give up. 'I often wonder whether America has trees like the ones in my drawing,' he hinted while enclosing a precocious crayon sketch. And in the next letter, 'If I came to America, do you think I might like it?' He was so enamoured of this approach that he copied that line into each of this three letters and sent them away.

It worked. His favourite 'parents', the ones who sent him Christmas presents, wrote to Sister Celine to say that they'd often wanted to see the little boy they'd 'adopted' but they'd never been able to manage a trip to India. Would it not be possible for young Joseph to be sent to America instead? As soon as they heard from Sister Celine, they would be happy to enclose an air-ticket for the little boy. Of course, they were not suggesting that he should stay with them always. Obviously, his place was amongst 'his people' in India and 'with you all at HELP'. They would send him back, but they did so want to see him, just once.

Sister Celine seemed a little taken aback by the letter. It was not customary for fosterparents to evince such an interest in their protégés. When they were old enough the children were simply taught an elementary trade and packed off to earn their keep. Foreign trips, for however short a duration, were highly unusual.

Sister Celine showed Joseph the letter and asked, 'You haven't been up to anything, have you?' To his excited protestations, she merely responded, 'We'll see.' And then she went to talk to Sister Eva.

Joseph had only seen one movie before. That was a documentary about HELP's activities among orphan children in the wilds of Bihar, and it had been shown one evening after dinner by the man who made it, so that the nuns could all see what the outside world was being told about their work. Sister Eva, in a spirit of generosity, had suggested that the boys, at least those over five, be permitted to sit on the ground and watch it too. It might teach them a few things, she told the other nuns, make them realise how much we do for them, maybe instil some gratitude in them. Joseph had fallen asleep halfway through that movie. He didn't want to see starving Adivasi children and warm-hearted nuns; he saw them every day. The black-and-white images, the →

A development project in the drought-stricken Upper East of Northern Ghana had brought fresh water from wells to the homes of the Frafra people.

Photo: Caroline Penn/ Impact

monotonous, superimposed voice of the commentator, blurred in his mind; the nuns danced tiptoe through the crevices of his brain, and the pictures pulsed and faded in his eyes. Firm but gentle hands were rousing him.

'Get up – it's time to go to bed.'

In the background, Sister Eva's high-pitched voice rang through the clear night: 'Look at them! Give them a special treat like this and half of them go to sleep! Don't ever let me catch any of you asking to see a movie again! I mean it!'

But what a movie this was. Bright, vivid colours, pretty, white women in short dresses, fast cars racing down broad, foreign streets. It was like nothing he had ever seen before. And he wanted to hear it; hear the loud roar of the car engines, the soft, tinkling laughter of the women, the shouts and the screams and all the sound of bullets and people whizzing aeroplanes.

'Sir'. The steward who had dispensed the earphones was standing at the end of the aisle, just behind Joseph, watching the movie too.

'Yes?'

'May I have some earphones too?'

'Of course.' The steward disappeared behind the partition and emerged with a polythene packet. He handed it to Joseph.

Joseph reached out to take it with an ineffable feeling of awe, wonder and achievement. He pushed aside the flap, put in his hand and touched the cold plastic. The sensation was indescribably thrilling.

'Two dollars and fifty cents, please.'

'But... but... I don't have any money,' Joseph said miserably. His eyes pleading with the steward. 'Please?'

The steward had a why-are-you-wasting-my-time-you-dumb-child look on his face. 'I'm sorry,' he said, taking the packet out of Joseph's hands, 'IATA regulations.'

And then he was gone, having invoked an authority higher than Joseph's longings, more powerful than philanthropy. When he re-emerged from the partition it was on the other side, on the aisle away from Joseph's.

Sister Eva had taken some time to decide. It was not that she minded in principle, she told Sister Celine, but this could set a dangerous precedent. The other children would be wanting to go too, and how many rich American fosterparents would be willing to mail them air-tickets.

In the end, however, to Joseph's great relief, she agreed. She would write personally to the American couple making it clear Joseph was not to be spoiled. And that he was to be back within a month, before he could be entirely corrupted by American ways, to resume his place among those as unfortunate as he was. Unless they wanted to keep him in America for good, which they showed no intention of doing.

The next few weeks passed in a frenzy of preparation. The ticket had to arrive, a flight had to be booked, a passport had to be issued to Joseph, a visa obtained. He was given a little suitcase for his clothes, and he swelled with pride at his tangible evidence of possessions. he had things, he was somebody. With a passport, a suitcase, a ticket, he was not just a little brown face in a crowd around the gruel bowl; he was Master Joseph Kumaran, and he was going somewhere.

And finally, wearing the tight blazer he had been given on the morning of his departure, its pocket stuffed with the newspaper clipping he had hoarded since it had been showed to him by Sister Celine four years ago, his passport nestling next to a glossy colour photo of his hosts sent to him so that he would recognise them at the airport, Joseph was put on board the plane. Sister Celine was there to see him off, she smiled at him through misty glasses, and Joseph felt the wetness on her cheeks when she hugged him at the departure gate. But he could not cry in return; he was a little scared, but more excited than upset, and he certainly was not sad.

The man sitting next to him did not care particularly for the movie after all. Twice, Joseph caught him dozing off, his eyes closing and his chin sinking slowly to his chest; twice, with equal suddenness, his neighbour's head would jerk awake, prompted, no doubt by some startling sound on the earphones. The third time this happened, the man pulled off his earphones in disgust and strode off, clambering over Joseph, in quest of a wash-basin.

Joseph could not resist this opportunity. It was too good to be true: earphones plugged in, next to him, unused. He eased himself out of his seatbelt and sat in his neighbour's chair. Then, tentatively, looking around him to make sure no one had noticed him, he raised the tips to his ears. Almost immediately he was assaulted by the sounds of the movie: brakes screeched as a car drew to a halt; a man dashed down some stairs with a gun in his hand; there was some panting dialogue; the gun went off, the bullet's report a deafening symphony in Joseph's ear; a woman screamed. And his neighbour returned from the toilet. →

Peering out from behind closed doors, this child in north Yemen keeps an eye on the camera.

Photo: Paul C Pet

Joseph looked up, almost in agony. His pleasure had been so brief. The man smiled down at him from the aisle. 'Mine, sonny,' he beamed. Joseph had been well brought up. 'Excuse me,' he said, gently removing the earphones and placing them on the seat. He slid into his place again, his neighbour returned to his chair, the earplugs went back on, and Joseph found he could not see the screen through his tears.

Hoping that his neighbour would notice, he dabbed at his eyes with the clean, white handkerchief Sister Angela had pressed into his hand that morning. That morning – it seemed so long ago. He returned the handkerchief to his pocket, feeling once again the magazine clipping that, four years ago, had started him on this journey. Resolutely, he refrained from pulling it out. That was not him: he had another identity now. He took out his passport, and his eyes caressed each detail on the inside page, from the fictional birthdate (It's easier that going through the entire "birthdate unknown" business,' Sister Eva had declared) to the inventory of his characteristics ('Hair: black; eyes: black; skin: brown') to the new, awkward photograph. Joseph staring glassy-eyed into the studio camera. And then, returning the passport at long last to his inside pocket, he touched the other photo, the glossy, colour portrait of his new, albeit temporary, parents. After some hesitation, he took it out: these were the people whose house he could call home for the next month.

But would he really? He stared at their forms in the photograph. They had sent Joseph their picture so he would recognise them, but they had not asked for his. 'We're sure we'll spot him as soon as he gets off the plane,' the wife had written to Sister Celine. 'We feel we've known him all our lives.' Joseph had felt flattered then, deeply touched. Then one day, in a fit of temper, Sister Eva had threatened to replace Joseph with another little dark-skinned boy from the orphanage. 'Do you think they'd be able to tell the difference?' she had demanded.

In silent, desperate misery, Joseph had not known what to say.

Looking at the photograph, Joseph tried to think of the magic of America, of things there he had heard about and dreamed of – movies, parties, delicious food of infinite variety, outings to the beach and to Disneyland. But his eyes dilated and the photograph blurred. He did not know why he felt suffused with a loneliness more intense, more bewildering in its sadness that he ever experienced in the gruel crowds of HELP. He was alone, lost somewhere between a crumpled magazine clipping and the glossy brightness of a colour photograph.

On the seat next to him, his neighbour snored peacefully, chin resting in surrender on his chest, earphones imbedded into the sides of his head. On the screen, magic images flickered, cascaded and danced on.

from **THE FIVE-DOLLAR SMILE** by Shashi Tharoor, in Penguin New Writing in India

Absorbing influences: surplus bowler hats were dumped in the Andes by a British firm in the nineteenth century, when they were first adopted by the indigenous peoples.

Photo:
Maximilian Bruggmann

ZAYNAB ALKALI
Nigeria

was born in 1950 to an Islamic family in a village in Borno State. She moved to a Christian village in Gongola State, where she was brought up. She graduated from Bayero University, Kano. The first woman novelist from Northern Nigeria, she teaches at the University of Maiduguri. She has written two novels, *The Stillborn* – a lively story of family life, centring on the adolescent Li and her hopes of independence – and *The Virtuous Woman*.

JORGE AMADO
Brazil

was born in Ilhéus in northeastern Brazil in 1912, the son of a cocoa planter. His early works were compelling pleas for social justice, culminating in his monumental *The Violent Land*, a panorama of the human cost of taming the coastal forests of Bahia for cocoa, the 'chocolate gold'. With *Gabriela, Clove and Cinnamon*, which appeared in Brazil in 1958, Amado turned to the more personal concerns that marked his subsequent writing. His greatest achievement, *Dona Flor and Her Two Husbands*, remains a perennial best seller in Brazil, where it was made into a film and television series: 'Dona Flor' coffeehouses and bars appeared in cities and villages throughout the country. In more than 20 volumes of novels and short stories, Amado evokes the life and spirit of a richly fascinating country.

ISABEL ALLENDE
Chile

was born in Lima, Peru in 1942 but considers Chile her native country. She lived there from childhood until her uncle, the socialist President Salvador Allende, was overthrown in a bloody military coup in 1973. She fled the country and went into exile in Venezuela. For several years she pursued the career in journalism she had started at the age of 17. Then in 1981 she turned her hand to writing a novel. The result was *The House of the Spirits*, which became an instant, worldwide best-seller. This novel alone has made her the most widely-read Latin American woman writer of all time. It was followed by *Of Love and Shadows, Eva Luna*, and *The Stories of Eva Luna*. Her latest book, *Paula*, is the true account of her own daughter who went into a coma several years ago. Isabel Allende now lives in California.

JUNG CHANG
China

was born in Yibin, Sichuan Province, China, in 1952. She was a Red Guard briefly at the age of 14 and then worked as a peasant, a 'barefoot doctor', a steelworker, and an electrician before becoming an English-language student and, later, an assistant lecturer at Sichuan University. She left China for Britain in 1978 and was subsequently awarded a scholarship by York University, where she obtained a PhD in Linguistics in 1982 – the first person from the People's Republic of China to receive a doctorate from a British university. Jung Chang lives in London and teaches at the School of Oriental and African Studies, London University.

DOMITILA BARRIOS DE CHUNGARA
Bolivia

was born in the mining village of Siglo XX in the Bolivian Andes in 1937. Her mother died when she was nine, and she became responsible for raising her four sisters in extreme poverty. Her father, an activist in the Movement Nacionalista Revolucionario, lost his job because of his political activities. When Domitila grew up she married a tin-miner and had seven children. During this time she became involved in the struggle of the Bolivian tin miners, organizing the women into an active force, and becoming herself a militant women's leader. Domitila recorded her development as a popular leader with the help of Brazilian journalist and social anthropologist Moema Viezzer. The result was the book *Let Me Speak!*

ANITA DESAI
India

was born in 1937; her father was Bengali and her mother German, and she was educated in Delhi. Her published work includes *Clear Light of Day*, which was shortlisted for the 1980 Booker Prize, *Fire on the Mountain*, for which she won the Royal Society of Literature's Winifred Holtby Memorial Prize and the 1978 National Academy of Letters Award, *In Custody*, which was shortlisted for the 1984 Booker Prize, *Baumgartner's Bombay* and *The Village by the Sea*. She has also written several books for children. She is a member of the Advisory Board for English of the National Academy of Letters in Delhi and a Fellow of the Royal Society of Literature in London. Anita Desai is married, has four children, and lives in India.

FANNY CARRIÓN DE FIERRO
Ecuador

received her doctorate in literature and linguistics from Pontificia Católica del Ecuador, Quito, in 1981. She is a visiting professor at Willamette University in Oregon. Her publications include numerous articles, essays and literary studies on subjects such as women's issues, human and children's rights, indigenous and grassroots movements, and linguistics. She has received many awards in Ecuador, among them the Gabriela Mistral National Poetry Award on several occasions, and the National Poetry Award.

CARLOS FUENTES
Mexico

grew up in Washington DC where his father was a counsellor at the Mexican Embassy. In 1975 Fuentes himself became the Mexican Ambassador in Paris. Novelist, diplomat and political thinker, he has also been the author of screenplays, a collaborator of Buñuel and a professor at Harvard and Cambridge. He has written many novels, including *The Old Gringo* (made into a film) and *Myself and Others*. His most celebrated novel – *Terra Nostra* – won the prestigious Rómula Gallegos Prize.

EDUARDO GALEANO
Uruguay

was born in Montevideo at the end of the winter of 1940. He is the author of a number of works which recover the American past – *The Open Veins of Latin America* and the trilogy *Memory of Fire* – and other books – *Days and Nights of Love and War, The Book of Embraces* – that explore the wonders and the horrors of everyday life. In *Las palabaras ardentes ('Burning words')* imagination flies where it will. He has also published two collections of his diaries and essays – *Nosotros decimos no ('We say no')* and subsequently *Ser como ellos y otros articulos ('To Be Like Them and Other Articles')* – and a few anthologies of his narrative work. His most recent work is *Football in Sun and Shadow*.

NADINE GORDIMER
South Africa

was born in 1923 in a small mining town called Springs in South Africa. From an early age she questioned her identity as a member of the minority white population of South Africa. Her childhood scrutiny of the world about her never waned. She is regarded by many as one of the most exceptional writers of fiction in the English language. An ardent opponent of apartheid, for a time her work was banned in South Africa. She became an member of the National Executive of the Congress of South African Writers, the African National Congress and a Vice President of International PEN. Among many other awards, in 1974 she shared the Booker Prize for *The Conversationist*, and was awarded the 1991 Nobel Prize for literature. She has published twenty novels and seven collections of short stories.

PALDEN GYATSO
Tibet

has been the longest-serving prisoner of the Chinese regime in Tibet. Captured in 1959 in the wake of the Lhasa protests, he has spent more than half his life in prisons and labour camps, the victim of torture and frequent beatings. On 29 September 1992 he arrived in Dharamsala, India, after 33 years of imprisonment. He presented the instruments of his torture to the Dalai Lama, who instructed him to tell his story to the world. Autobiography is a form of literature unknown to Tibetan culture. The lives of the Great Lamas and Rinpoches are written by their followers many years after their deaths, but no living Tibetan writes their own life story. Palden has only done so because of the express request of the Dalai Lama. He has travelled the world as the focus of an Amnesty International Campaign.

CHRISTOPHER HAMPTON
England

spent much of his childhood in Zanzibar. His first stage play, *When Did You Last See My Mother?*, was written when he was 17 and was performed at the Royal Court Theatre in London while he was still a student at Oxford. His subsequent career as a prominent dramatist and screen writer has included original works such as *The Philanthropist,* and translations and adaptations. The screenplay for *Dangerous Liaisons* won him an Oscar. *Savages* is based on the brutal treatment the Xingu peoples of the Amazon during the 1960s, and on the record of their myths.

BESSIE HEAD
Botswana

was born in 1937 in South Africa, daughter of a white mother and a black father. She migrated to Botswana in her early twenties, rejecting the legalities and ethics of apartheid which had forced her – as 'a Coloured' – to be brought up in foster homes and restricted her teaching to a segregated school. She took her only son across the border and waited 14 years to gain Botswanan citizenship. An extraordinary and prolific writer, Bessie Head wished to be ordinary, to live simply among villagers, away from political tensions and élitist domination. Her writing reflects this interest, but also her own traumatic experience of rejection. Bessie Head's many books include: *When Rain Clouds Gather, Maru, Serowe: Village of the Rain Wind, A Question of Power, Tales of Tenderness and Power, A Woman Alone* and *Gesture of Belonging.* She died in 1986.

LILIANA HECKER
Argentina

was born in 1943. While still a teenager she published her first collection of short stories, *Los que vivieron la zarza.* She edited the literary review *El Ornitorrinco* (formerly *El Escarabajo de Oro*) during the 1970s, a difficult decade for all forms of expression in Argentina. Her latest novel is *Zona de Clivaje.*

HEINZ INSU FENKL
Korea

left Korea when he was 12 years old. His family eventually settled in Castroville, California. An award-winning writer and translator, and a former Fulbright Scholar in Korea, he now teaches creative writing, Asian-American literature and Korean literature at Vassar College. He lives in Poughkeepsie, New York.

SITIVENI KALOUNIVITI
Fiji

was born in the province of Bua on the island of Vanua Levu, the son of a villager and a rural medical nurse. He worked for a time with Radio Fiji.

GOHAR KORDI
Iran

lives in London with her husband and son. Her story, *'From Missionary School to Mitcham'*, appeared in the anthology *So Very English*; her autobiographical novel *An Iranian Odyssey*, was published the following year (1991). She has written a television film script called *An Iranian Childhood*. Her story, *'I Was Touched'*, appeared in *Mustn't Grumble: Writing by Disabled Women*, and she has also written a short story, *'Hold the Word'*, for *Bought to Book*. She has been working on a stage play and another novel.

CAMARA LAYE
Guinea

was born in 1926. A child of intellectual promise, he went first to the technical college at Conakry, the capital of Guinea, and later to France to study engineering. In Paris he found a totally different culture and, lonely and unhappy, wrote his first book, *The African Child*. This largely autobiographical work tells the story of his childhood among the Malinke people, surrounded by ritual magic and superstition, and his emergence into manhood and independence. Twelve years later, having returned to his native land, he wrote *A Dream of Africa*. In this sequel to *The African Child*, the narrator — now influenced by his experiences in Europe — sees an Africa on the violent brink of independence.

OSWALD MBUYISEMI MTSHALI
South Africa

was born in 1940 in South Africa and lives in Johannesburg.

RIGOBERTA MENCHÚ
Guatemala

was brought up in rural Guatemala where, like many other Indian communities in Latin America, she faced gross injustice and exploitation. She decided at an early age to learn Spanish and then turned to catechist activity as much as an expression of social revolt as of her deep religious belief. After the coming to power of the Garcia Lucas regime in 1978, her brother, father and mother were killed in separate, horrifying incidents of savagery by the army. She rose to prominence as a national leader of the resistance. Her story, *I... Rigoberta Menchú*, is the result of a programme of interviews by Elizabeth Burgos Debray. In 1992 she was awarded the Nobel Peace Prize.

SUNITI NAMJOSHI
India

was born in Bombay in 1941, leaving India for the West in 1968. She has taught at universities in India and Canada. She has published numerous poems, fables, and articles and reviews in anthologies, collections and Women's Studies journals in India, Canada and Britain. Her books include *Feminist Fables, The Conversations of Cow, Aditi and the One-Eyed Monkey, The Blue Donkey Fables, Because of India: Selected Poems, The Mothers of Maya Diip* and *Saint Suniti and the Dragon.* She is renowned for her command of the modern fable genre, her humour and originality. She lives in Devon, England, and has been working on *Building Babel*, which is about the process of building a culture. The final chapter is on the Internet as a kind of building site to which others can contribute.

NGŨGĨ WA THIONG'O
Kenya

was born in Limuru, Kenya, in 1938. He was educated at the Alliance High School, Kikuyu, at Makerere University, Uganda and at the University of Leeds. His novels include *Weep Not, Child, The River Between, A Grain of Wheat* and *Petals of Blood. Devils on the Cross* was conceived and written during one year's detention in prison in Kenya, where he was held without trial after the performance by peasants and workers of his play *Ngaahika Ndeenda ('I will Marry When I Want')*. This was the first of his novels to be published in his own language and then translated into English and many other languages. He has also written collections of short stories, plays and numerous essays. He is an active campaigner for African language and form and he writes, travels and lectures extensively on this theme.

BEN OKRI
Nigeria

the poet, novelist and short-story writer, was born in the small town of Minna, Nigeria, in 1959. He lived through civil war and political turmoil that ultimately drove him to England, where he studied comparative literature at the University of Essex. He has since published ten books, including two volumes of short stories, *Incidents at the Shrine* and *Stars of the New Curfew*. His most recent book, *Dangerous Love*, was published in 1996. He has won many prizes, including the Paris Review Aga Khan prize for fiction, and the Booker Prize in 1991 for his novel *The Famished Road.*

PRAMOEDYA ANANTA TOER
Indonesia

was born on the island of Java in 1925. He was imprisoned first by the Dutch from 1947 to 1949 for his role in the Indonesian revolution, then by the Indonesian Government as a political prisoner. Many of his works have been written while in prison, including the *Buru Quartet (This Earth of Mankind, Child of All Nations, Footsteps* and *House of Glass)* which was conceived in stories he told to other prisoners during his confinement on Buru Island from 1965 to 1979. He is the author of 30 works of fiction and nonfiction. He received the PEN Freedom-to-write award in 1988. He is currently under city arrest in Jakarta where his books are banned and selling them a crime punishable by imprisonment.

CECIL RAJENDRA
Malaysia

was born in Penang and spent the best part of his childhood in the fishing village of Tanjong Tokong. He qualified as a barrister at Lincoln's Inn, London, in 1968. In the early 1970s he initiated a cultural forum in the basement of the Troubadour Coffee House on the Old Brompton Road, London, and teamed up with Cecil Roberts from Sierra Leone and Helio Diaz Pinto from Brazil to form Third World Troubadours. He now lives in Penang and started Malaysia's first rural legal aid centre for farmers, fisherfolk and factory workers. His other passions include soccer, music, Tantra, art and non-partisan politics. He has published 13 collections of poetry.

ASTRID ROEMER
Surinam

was born in 1947 in Parimaribo, Surinam, and trained as a teacher. She has worked mainly as a journalist. From 1966 to 1975 she travelled between Surinam and the Netherlands. Involved with working against racism, she said: 'Through literature I'm trying little by little to reach the continent of my ancestors...' She has published fiction and non-fiction in both Dutch and Sranen.

ARUNDHATI ROY
India

was trained as an architect. She has worked as a production designer and written the screenplay for two films. She lives in New Delhi. *The God of Small Things,* her first novel, won the Booker Prize in 1997.

SULEKHA SANYAL

Bangladesh

was born in 1928 in Korkandi, a village now in Bangladesh. Before going to school she was taught by her father and uncle. A childless aunt then took her to live with her in Chittagong and sent her to school there. Her first writing appeared in the children's section of the newspaper *Yugantar*. In 1942, when Chittagong was bombed, she returned to Korkandi and completed her high school there. Later she went to Calcutta, where she graduated from Scottish Church College. An important intellectual influence was that of the philosopher Ramtanu Lahiri, who belonged to her mother's family and whose agnostic humanism she eagerly absorbed. She was introduced to socialism by her brother and his friends, and in 1948 and 1949 she actively participated in the political movements in Bengal, when she was imprisoned for the first time. Her first story, *'Pankatilak' ('Marked with Slime')* was published in the journal *Arani* in 1944. In 1947 she moved to India, where she struggled to survive as a refugee. In 1957 she was afflicted with leukemia. She kept writing until her premature death in 1962. Her published works include the novel *Nabankur,* a collection of short stories *Sindure Megh ('Red Clouds'),* and *Dewal Padma ('Wall Flower')* a novel published posthumously in 1964.

OLIVE SENIOR

Jamaica

was born in 1941 and grew up in rural Jamaica. Many of her stories reflect that experience. She has been editor of the *Jamaica Journal* for several years. In 1985 she published a collection of poems, *Talking of Trees,* and a book of short stories, *Summer Lightning,* which won the Commonwealth Literature Prize.

WOLE SOYINKA

Nigeria

was born in 1934. He was educated at Government College, Ibadan and then at England's Leeds University, and worked in British theatre before returning to Nigeria in 1960. His earlier prose works include *The Interpreters* and the acclaimed *Death and the King's Horseman.* In 1986 he became the first African writer to win the Nobel Prize for Literature. He is currently Woodruff Professor of the Arts at Emory University, Atlanta, US.

LOURDES TEODORO

Brazil

born in Brazil in the 1930s, she is a professor at the Institute of Architecture at the University of Brasilia and the author of several books of poetry, including *Agua-Merinha Ou Tempo Sem Palavra.*

SHASHI THAROOR

(India)

was born in London in 1956 and grew up in Bombay and Calcutta. He holds a PhD from the Fletcher School of Law and Diplomacy at Tufts University. He has worked at the United Nations since 1978, serving 11 years with the UN High Commissioner for Refugees. Among his many publications are *The Great Indian Novel, The Five-Dollar Smile and Other Stories* and *Show Business.* He is currently Executive Assistant to the Secretary-general of the United Nations.

CHARITY WACIUMA

Kenya

grew up during the seven years of the Mau Mau Emergency. Her parents were both pioneers: they ran away from home to get a Western education, then as adults promoted public health and education for the Kenyan people and recognition for women. Waciuma herself is a literary advocate of reason and patience, writing frankly of women's role in Kenya yet with a philosophical acceptance of the time required for change. Her children's books include *Mweru the Ostrich Girl, The Golden Feather* and *Merry-making.*

SHAHIDUL ALAM, Drik Picture Library, 58, Road 15A Dhanmondi RA, Dhaka 1209, Bangladesh, Tel: (+880) 328332, Fax (+880) 2 863470, e-mail shahidul@drik.net
Photos on pages 39, 80, 81

ERIC BACHMANN, Hauptgasse 77, CH-5466 Kaiserstuhl, Switzerland, Tel/Fax: (+41) 1 858 26 27
Photo on page 85

HERMAN BERTIAU, Rue A Bréart 47, B-1060 Brussels, Belgium, Tel: (+32) 2 5378186
Photo on page 19

MAXIMILIAN BRUGGMANN, Rue Condémines 21, CH-1400 Yverdon-Les-Bains, Switzerland, Tel/Fax: (+41) 24 425 97 70
Photo on page 115

KATHRIN BUECHLER, Unterer Rheinweg 114, CH-4057 Basel, Switzerland, Tel: (+41) 61 692 10 17
Photo on page 53

PIERS CAVENDISH, Impact Photo Agency, 26/27 Great Sutton Street, London EC1V 0DX, UK, Tel: (+44) 171 251 5091, Fax: (+44) 171 608 0114
Photo on page 41

HANSRUEDI DÖRIG, Agnesstrasse 2, CH-8004 Zurich, Switzerland, Tel: (+41) 1 241 8052
Photos on pages 75, 101

SARAH ERRINGTON, The Hutchison Library, 118b Holland Park Avenue, London W11, UK, Tel: (+44) 171 229 2743, Fax: (+44) 171 792 0259
Photo on page 29

JULIO ETCHART, Reportage, 28 Norcott Road, London N16 7EL, UK, Tel: (+44) 181 806 9803, Fax: (+44) 181 806 6980
Photos on pages 31, 59, 83

ANGELA FISHER, Robert Estall Picture Library, Falcon House, 12-14 Swan Sreet, Boxford, Sudbury, Suffolk, CO10 5NZ, UK, Tel: (+44) 1787 210 111, Fax: (+44) 1787 211 440
Photo on page 27

ANDREW FOREST, Environmental Images, 40 Bowling Green Lane, London EC1R 0NE, UK, Tel: (+44) 171 833 1355 Fax: (+44) 171 713 6348
Photo on page 43

SALLY & RICHARD GREENHILL, 357A Liverpool Road, London N1 1NL, UK, Tel: (+44) 171 607 8549
Photo on page 47

IVO HENDRIKX, Wilde Tijmstraat 33, B-3600 Genk, Belgium
Photo on page 69

MARY JELIFFE, Sparrows House, Honeybottom, Near Bagnor, Newbury, Berkshire RG16 8AL, UK, Tel: (+44) 1635 47067
Photos on pages 17, 99

NASROLAH KASRAIAN, Milkenstrasse 3, CH-3150 Schwarzenburg, Switzerland, Tel: (+41) 31 731 0871
Photo on page 79

THOMAS KELLY, TCS/The Cover Story, Weesperzijde 103, NL-1091 EM Amsterdam, The Netherlands, Tel: (+31) 20 663 0740, Fax: (+31) 20 693 2706
Photo on page 73

M&A KIRTLEY, Agence ANA, 6 Avenue René-Coty, F-75014 Paris, France, Tel: (+33) 43 22 62 11, Fax: (+33) 43 35 28 38
Photo on page 61

THOMAS LAIRD, TCS/The Cover Story, Weesperzijde 103, NL-1091 EM Amesterdam, The Netherlands, Tel: (+31) 20 663 0740, Fax: (+31) 20 693 2706
Photo on page 65

MICHAEL MACINTYRE, The Hutchison Library, 118b Holland Park Avenue, London W11, UK, Tel: (+44) 171 229 2743, Fax: (+44) 171 792 0259
Photo on page 97

STEVE MORGAN, Environmental Images, 40 Bowling Green Lane, London EC1R 0NE, UK, Tel: (+44) 171 833 1355 Fax: (+44) 171 713 6348
Photo on page 103

JAMES NELSON, Da Costakade 71/111, NL-1053 WH Amsterdam, The Netherlands, Tel: (+31) 20 616 6588, Fax: (+31) 20 689 5688
Photo on page 21

IAN OSBORN, Footprints Colour Picture Library, Goldfin Cottage, Maidlands Farm, Broad Oak, Rye, East Sussex TN31 6BJ, UK, Tel/Fax: (+44) 1424 883078
Photo on cover and titlepage

CAROLINE PENN, Impact Photo Agency, 26-27 Great Sutton Street, London EC1V 0DX, UK, Tel: (+44) 171 251 5091, Fax: (+44) 171 608 0114
Photo on page 111

PAUL C PET
46, Herrengracht, NL-Amsterdam, The Netherlands, Tel: (+31) 20 625 8032
Photo on page 113

JESCO VON PUTTKAMER, The Hutchison Library, 118b Holland Park Avenue, London W11, UK, Tel: (+44) 171 229 2743, Fax: (+44) 171 792 0259
Photo on page 63

DAVID RANSOM, New Internationalist, 55 Rectory Rd, OX4 1BW, Oxford, UK, Tel: (+44) 1865 728 181, Fax: (+44) 1865 793 152
Photo on page 55

PAUL VAN RIEL, Robert Harding Picture Library, 58-59 Great Malborough Street, London W1V 1DD, UK, Tel: (+44) 171 287 5414, Fax: (+44) 171 631 1070
Photo on page 45

ULRICH SCHWEIZER, Villars le Grand, CH-1584 Villars, Switzerland, Tel: (+41) 37 7723 20
Photo on page 33

SEAN SUTTON, North View, Ireby, Cumbria CAE 1DX, UK, Tel: (+44) 16973 71698
Photo on page 77

MICHEL SZLUC-KRZYZANOWSKI, Derde Helmerstraat 6, NL-1054 BG Amsterdam, The Netherlands, Tel: (+31) 20 6127077, Fax: (+33) 20 616 1224
Photo on page 23

STÉPHAN TORRE, 8 Chemin de la Redoute, CH-1260 Nyon, Switzerland, Tel: (+41) 22 362 7881
Photo on page 95

AMEDEO VERGANI, Via Girolamo Emiliani 6, I-22046 Merone, Italy, Tel: (+39) 31 650 423, Fax: (+39) 31 650 588
Photo on pages 37, 49, 89, 93,

JANET WISHNETSKY, 34 Rue de l'Aurore, B-1000 Brussels, Belgium
Photo on page 25, 107

ACKNOWLEDGEMENTS

ZAYNAB ALKALI: from The Stillborn, 1984, reprinted by permission of Addison Wesley Longman Ltd.

JORGE AMADO: from Dona Flor and Her Two Sisters, translated by Harriet de Onis, 1986, Serpents Tail, London and Alfred A Knopf, Inc, New York.

ISABEL ALLENDE: from Eva Luna, 1987, Alfred A Knopf Inc, New York.

JUNG CHANG: from Wild Swans, 1991, Harper Collins, London.

DOMITILA BARRIOS DE CHUNGARA: from Let Me Speak!, 1978, Monthly Review Press, New York, and Stage 1, London.

ANITA DESAI: from Games at Twilight, 1978, Heinemann, Oxford. Copyright with the author, c/o Rogers, Coleridge and White, London.

FANNY CARRIÓN DE FIERRO: from 'Grain of Sand', translated by Sally Cheney Bell, in These Are Not Sweet Girls, ed. Marjorie Agosin, 1994, White Pine Press, Fredonia, New York.

CARLOS FUENTES: from Christopher Unborn, 1989, André Deutsch Ltd, London.

EDUARDO GALEANO: reprinted with permission of the author from The Book of Embraces, translated by Cedric Belfrage, 1991, WW Norton, New York and London, and from Football in Sun and Shadow, translated by Mark Fried, 1997, Fourth Estate, London

NADINE GORDIMER: 'Country Lovers' from A Soldier's Embrace, 1980, Jonathan Cape, London.

PALDEN GYATSO: from Fire Under the Snow, translated by Palden Gyatso and Tsering Shakya, 1997, The Harvill Press, London.

CHRISTOPHER HAMPTON: from Savages, 1974, Faber and Faber, London.

BESSIE HEAD: from Tales of Tenderness and Power, 1989, Heinemann, Oxford.

LILIANA HECKER: from 'Berkley or Mariana of the Universe', translated by Alberto Manguel, in The Magic and the Real: Short Stories by Latin American Women, ed Celia Correas de Zapata, 1988, Arte Público Press, Huston.

HEINZ INSU FENKL: from Memories of my Ghost Brother, 1997, Anchor, London.

SITIVENI KALOUNIVITI: from 'A Childhood Experience' in Creative Writing from Fiji, 1985, Fiji Writers' Association, Suva.

GOHAR KORDI: from Mahi's Story, 1995, The Women's Press, London.

CAMARA LAYE: from The African Child, 1954, Fontana, London.

OSWALD MBUYISEMI MTSHALI: 'Boy on a swing' from Poems of Black Africa, ed Wole Soyinka, 1975, Heinemann, Oxford.

RIGOBERTA MENCHÚ: from I... Rigoberta Menchú. An Indian Woman in Guatemala, translated by Ann Wright, 1984, Verso, London.

SUNITI NAMJOSHI: from Saint Suniti & the Dragon, and Other Fables, 1994, Virago, London.

NGŨGĨ WA THIONG'O: from Weep Not, Child, translated by James Kirkup, 1964, Heinemann, Oxford.

BEN OKRI: from The Famished Road, 1991, Jonathan Cape, London.

PRAMOEDYA ANANTA TOER: from Footsteps, translated by Max Lane, 1990, Penguin Books, London.

CECIL RAJENDRA: from Broken Buds, 1994, The Other India Press, Goa.

ASTRID ROEMER: from 'A Name For Love', translated by Rita Gircoor, in Daughters of Africa, ed Margaret Busby, 1992, Jonathan Cape, London.

ARUNDHATI ROY: from The God of Small Things, 1997, Flamingo, London.

SULHEKA SANYAL: from 'Nabankur (The Germinating Seed)', translated by Madhuchanda Karlekar, in Women Writing in India, vol II, ed Susie Tharu and K Lalita, 1993, Pandora, London.

OLIVE SENIOR: from 'The Two Grandmothers' in Arrival of the Snake Woman and Other Stories, 1989, Longman, Harlow.

WOLE SOYINKA: from Ibadan, 1995, Minerva, London.

LOURDES TEODORO: 'The Generation of Fear' from Agua-Marinha ou Tempo sem Palavra, translated by Iain Bruce, in Daughters of Africa, ed Margaret Busby, 1992, Jonathan Cape, London.

SHASHI THAROOR: from 'The Five-Dollar Smile' in Penguin New Writing in India, ed Aditya Behl and David Nicholls, 1992, Penguin Books, New Delhi.

CHARITY WACIUMA: from 'Daughters of Mumbi' in Unwinding Threads; Writing by Women in Africa, ed Charlotte H Bruner, 1994, Heinemann, Oxford.

Every effort has been made to trace all copyright holders and to clear reprint permissions. This process has been complicated and if any required acknowledgements have been overlooked it is unintentional. If notified, the publishers will be pleased to rectify any omission in future editions.